John Ericsson and the Engines of Exile

For Lo
with all good wishes!

By David Mel Paul

Chandler Lake Books

Traverse City, MI

John Ericsson and the Engines of Exile

Crediting Sources

Every effort has been made to credit the appropriate source for each of the many documents cited in this book. If the author has omitted referencing any proper source he will be glad to add it to all subsequent printings of this book, an addition that the new just-in-time book printing methods facilitate. You are invited to send corrections and comments to the author, David Mel Paul, P.O. Box 40806, Washington, DC 20016 USA.

ISBN: 978-1-943338-10-8

Library of Congress Control Number: 2016947588

Published by Chandler Lake Books
2554 Chandler Road, Traverse City, MI

Printed in the United States of America.

To my wife

Margareta

and to the beloved memory of

David M. Paul, Sr.

Vivan Caap

Contents

Acknowledgments

It is a joy to thank Donna Martin, who, on retiring from a remarkable career culminating as vice president and editorial director of a Midwest publishing firm with global distribution, has continued producing fine books under her own imprint. Through the processes and the intricacies, both old and new, now required to transform a manuscript into a published book, she has been my indefatigable guide and counselor.

My research into Ericsson's life began in 2000 at home in Washington, DC, with the extraordinary resources of the Library of Congress, especially the Manuscripts Division headed by James H. Hutson, with advice from Leonard C. Bruno, manuscript historian in science & technology. It soon extended to the American Swedish Historical Museum in Philadelphia, where Margaretha Talerman, then curator, welcomed my wife Margareta and me to the extensive Ericsson holdings, including a major collection of the inventor's correspondence. Talerman is an accomplished Ericsson scholar herself. The museum's collection of John Ericsson's letters had been catalogued by the late Esther Chilström Meixner. Earlier, it was Dr. Meixner who, knowing me to be a translator of Swedish, suggested that the letters between Ericsson and his natural son, Hjalmar Elworth, would be of great interest to me. It was a while before I realized it, but she had handed me a key to the enigmatic character of John Ericsson.

My wife's Swedish family have welcomed us back regularly for visits to Swedish collections of Ericssoniana. I found many Ericsson documents in Stockholm, but also in Gävle, Linköping, Norrköping, Göteborg, Vadstena, Malmö and Lund.

I was especially interested in learning more about Hjalmar Elworth, John's natural son, and Robert Herpai, archivist at the Swedish Railway Museum in Gävle, welcomed me with many artifacts of Elworth's distinguished railroad career. But the treasure of the collection was Hjalmar's handwritten travel journal, in a small bound notebook, of his 1876 travels across America and back, on our new transcontinental railroad, after he had visited our Centennial Exhibition in Philadelphia as a showcase of railroad technology.

In Stockholm, Eva Dillman, librarian of the Manuscripts Division in the Royal Library, repeatedly eased my access to their comprehensive collection of Ericsson's correspondence with Swedish military and civil officials, including both his brother Nils and, after their first meeting in 1876, with his own son.

The National Museum of Science and Technology in Stockholm has an excellent Ericsson collection as well, and its then librarian, Inger Björklund, facilitated my study of many accounts of Ericsson's life in Sweden. More recently, through the efforts of her successor, Eva Derlow, permission was granted me for brief quotations from Elworth and Ericsson biographical articles in *Daedalus*, the museum's yearbooks of 1957, 1966 and 1967. In 2003, on the centenary of Ericsson's birth, the museum published a splendid illustrated tribute to Ericsson by the late Björn Hallerdt. Derlow has very kindly arranged for "Tekniska" to grant me permission for a quotation from Hallerdt I reshaped into a succinct chronology of Ericsson's life in 3 countries.

The quality of support my research has received from Swedish librarians, archivists, curators and others testifies to Ericsson's special position in Sweden's vigorous memory. To Tommy Westergren at the Royal Institute of Technology Library in Stockholm I am indebted for advice about Ericsson holdings in the capital, and for the privilege of viewing one of the only perfectly preserved copies of Ericsson's magnificent, self-published compendium of his own inventions, *Contributions to the Centennial Exhibition*. Johan T. Adelswärd sent me a copy of his ancestor Baron Adelswärd's letter home relating John Ericsson's generous hospitality when the young man paid a call on the famous inventor during a visit to New York. Karin Ek, archivist of the County Archives of Vadstena, found me Olof Ericsson's pay records from the Göta Kanal company. Per Restadh of SJ, the Swedish rail network of today, filled in details of Nils Ericson's accomplishments as the network's still-venerated founder, and of his protégé, John Ericsson's son Hjalmar. Anders Larsson, of the Manuscripts Department at Gothenburg University's library, generously provided copies of six key letters between John Ericsson and his close friend and business partner, Adolf von Rosen. Anne Wiktorsson, archivist of the Royal Swedish Academy of Sciences, readily furnished a copy of the autobiographical statement Nils Ericson submitted after being elected to that august body. Lars-Olof Skoglund, archivist of the Royal Swedish Medals office, provided key details of the ceremony in which Hjalmar was decorated by the Swedish king. Leif Ekström of the Holmen Paper Company sent me an article tracing the company's early acquisition of the same Vargön paper pulp factory whose failure in the 1880s ravaged the economies of Baron Nils Ericson's widow and three sons. Christer Olausson, assistant in the Gothenburg Maritime Museum, responded vividly to my need for visual details to limn the last Swedish scene young John Ericsson would ever see as his tall ship sailed out of Gothenburg's harbor toward England in 1826.

England, too, remembers him. Carol Morgan of England's Institution of Civil Engineers located and copied the minutes of a February 20, 1827 meeting of ICE for presentation of a paper about "Employing the Combustion of Fuel as a Moving Power" by "J. Ericsson, Lieutenant in the Swedish Army" soon after his arrival in London, and sent along the anonymously translated text of the aspiring young inventor's paper as well.

Swedish is considered a difficult language, but I have found word processing languages and digital mechanics much harder. My sons, Daniel, Frederic and David William Paul, are my computer experts—loving thanks, Dan, Fred, and Dave!

This acknowledgment concludes with warm thanks to Margaretha Runvik, now Margaretha R. Wickberg, whose devotion to John Ericsson inspired her to search out many overlooked details about Ericsson's early life in Sweden, but also about the farseeing project that in his last years engaged the inventor's whole attention, the conversion of sunlight into usable energy. Margaretha Runvik published *John Ericsson – Resan Mot Solen* [*John Ericsson – Voyage Toward the Sun*], a biography that was a frequent and grateful resort of mine during the years of my own research. She has kindly permitted me to include brief quotations from her Swedish text, in my own English translation, in this book.

Every effort has been made to contact the copyright holders of the many published resources that have enriched my interpretation of John Ericsson in this biography, when any excerpt was quoted. Rights holders of any publication not credited here should contact the author at P.O. Box 40806, Washington, DC 20016, USA, in order for a correction to be made in the next reprinting of the work.

David Mel Paul
January 2016, Washington, DC

Life of John Ericsson

A boy from Långbanshyttan village in the mining district of Värmland province, Sweden
1803-1810

Along the Göta Canal - Forsvik and Hajstorp, Sweden
1810-1821

Rifleman and Surveyor in Jämtland province, Sweden
1821-1826

Inventor on credit in London, England
1826-1839

Immigrant, "ingenious mechanic," and American hero in New York
1839-1889

Prologue

In 1861 The War came home, even to those who called it The Rebellion.

"The defeated troops...return to Washington baffled, humiliated, panic-struck. Where are your banners, and your bands of music, and your ropes to bring back your prisoners? Well, there isn't a band playing – and there isn't a flag but clings ashamed and lank to its staff," Walt Whitman wrote, after First Bull Run.

"Meantime...among the great persons and their entourage, a mixture of awful consternation, uncertainty, rage, shame, helplessness and stupefying disappointment. The worst is not only imminent, but already here."[1]

Seven months later, this dread coalesced around the nightmare shape of the *Merrimack*, a warship Union forces had tried to burn when forced to evacuate the Norfolk Navy Yard, but that was now being awfully resurrected by the rebels into a floating fortress of iron that the wooden warships blockading all the Southern ports might not be able to contain. And should it break free, Washington, Baltimore, Philadelphia, New York, Boston – would any Union harbor be safe? And it was said that France and England only waited for an opening in the blockade to rush support to the Confederacy.

On March 8, 1862, the news from Hampton Roads confirmed the North's worst fears: the warship *Cumberland* sunk, the *Congress* burned, the *Minnesota* driven aground and seemingly incapable of defense against a renewed attack by the armored colossus anticipated at dawn.

In the White House, President Lincoln was huddling with Stanton and Welles, secretaries of war and navy, and Stanton could hardly attend to the worries of his president, what with running to the windows to see whether the dreadnought of rebellion had not already lunged up the Potomac to lay waste the capital.[2]

It was in the sickly glare of panic that John Ericsson's *Monitor* appeared at Hampton Roads. The thousands watching from the hills and shores around Hampton Roads could not have failed to pity the little Union gunship that now interposed between the Confederate *Merrimack* and the U.S. frigate *Minnesota* paralyzed on its mud-bank. The *Merrimack*, whose hull was almost one hundred feet longer than that of the *Monitor*, made the newcomer appear not just an underdog, but a pathetic sacrifice, short work for the giant. Yet when the midget survived the *Merrimack's* first salvo of cannon fire and fired back, David and Goliath might instead have sprung to mind.

As the duel stretched on hour after hour, witnesses may have thought of another kind of armored contest none of them had seen, but many had read about in romances of the time – the clash of knights in armor.

Could the terrible schism in the nation be settled gallantly by these proxies, these champions of North and South, in single combat?

After four hours the giant gave up the attack. At least to the thousands of Union onlookers, the *Merrimack* seemed to slink away. Before their very eyes, a kind of Merlin magic of warfare seemed to have been practiced. *Monitor* seemed to have vanquished the rebel dreadnought that had sunk the *U.S.S. Cumberland* and burnt the *U.S.S. Congress*.

Vanquished Goliath safely, almost cleanly. In this four-hour battle not a single life had been lost in either vessel, a stark contrast to the recent hand-to-hand savagery of the armies.

But *Monitor* did not pursue and sink its giant adversary (to Ericsson's secret furious dismay; with time, that omission would swell up to dreadnought proportions). For the moment, however, all eyes were on John Ericsson's *Monitor*.

Not for the last time, there was a sudden unreasonable hope that "surgical strikes" magically directed to the very heart of the enemy could be launched with cold authority. Science had arrived as the *deus ex machina* of warfare. Soon a journalist described the *Monitor* as "a prodigy, and beautiful, scientific vessel."[3]

This illusion could hardly have lasted, since less than six months later the one-day disaster at Fredericksburg on December 13, 1862 cost the Union 12,650 dead, wounded, missing and captured.[4] But the illusion and its euphoria lasted long enough for the public to regard the *Monitor*'s inventor as the founder of what might be called the "science" of combat. For a time John Ericsson would be treated as almost a saint of technology whose magical intercession would assure success. Or, as Union General John Ellis Wool, among the rapt spectators at Hampton Roads, pronounced him, "the greatest man living."[5]

———

NOTES
1. Whitman, Walt, 1883, 23-4.
2. Welles, Gideon, 1960, i, 62-7.
3. White, Ruth, 1960, 218.
4. *Encyclopedia Britannica* 1957, ix, 728.
5. Stimers, Alban C., to John Ericsson, 1862, in Church, William C. 1906, i, 290.

I

Man of War

CHAPTER 1

A scale model of the warship *U.S.S. Monitor*, it was made all of gold. It rested on a table around which a group of gentlemen stood conversing and preening on an autumn evening in 1862. They had gathered to present this golden gift to the *Monitor*'s inventor, John Ericsson.[1]

The gentlemen around the table that autumn evening knew each other so well that there was no reason to record their names. They had each played a role in the Hampton Roads success of the *Monitor*, which had led within three weeks to a contract from the Navy to produce 10 more ironclads of the same kind with various improvements. Ericsson himself was one of the four "Battery Associates" named in the contract, so he owned a quarter share of the impending profits. Cornelius Delamater, whom Ericsson called "Harry," had been building Ericsson inventions for over twenty years. He was not a partner but a beneficiary nevertheless; Delamater Ironworks, builder of the main engines, boilers, propeller and other machinery of the first *Monitor*, would produce the same for the 10 vessels to come. Young Thomas Rowland would be there representing his Continental Ironworks, that had made the *Monitor*'s hull. Veteran Horatio Allen would have come from the Novelty Ironworks, that constructed the turret. And there would have been someone in the party from Clute & Brothers, who had built the turret engines, gun carriages, anchor windlass and engine room grates. John Ericsson's partners in the *Monitor* contract surely took part, moneymen John Winslow and John Griswold, from Troy, N.Y., and Cornelius Bushnell from New Haven, Connecticut, the man with the important contacts in the Navy and the White House.[2]

Some of the Navy officers who, spurred by President Lincoln, had overcome their misgivings and chosen Ericsson's unorthodox design may have accompanied Assistant Secretary of the Navy Gustavus Fox, but they were probably not among the donors of the golden *Monitor*.

The gleaming scale model on the table represented John Ericsson's lethal weapon system, except that the full-scale fighting machine was largely made of iron, while the model was made entirely of gold. Though it was faithful in external detail, it had no means to bombard and so was harmless as a tin soldier. As its truth to the real machine was somewhat ambiguous, its function must have gone beyond sheer representation.

There *was* a real scale model, and late the previous year Bushnell had used it to good effect with his high placed contacts; but it had been put together by the inventor. Ericsson had made it of pasteboard (even less like iron), yet at the critical moments, before the Ironclad Board of the Navy, in the hands of President Lincoln, it conveyed the truth of Ericsson's revolutionary insights into what a floating artillery battery should present to the enemy above, and what preserve below the waterline.[3]

Ericsson could be said to think in models, to think in intense detail, real detail, not theory. Never trained in theory, he had become a virtuoso at cut-and-try. And that took models, to work out every detail.

Long before, in the village of Långbanshyttan, Sweden, where John Ericsson's father Olof had been the manager of an iron mine, the little boy made his first models; one of them was of the mine itself, including men with little sledgehammers in the pit below, and above the surface a wheel that rotated to hoist the ore. In his last, eighth decade Ericsson would still be making models, miniature working solar engines that demonstrated how the sun's heat could be collected and concentrated with mirrors and put to work. Today, a few months after the *Monitor*'s triumph, he was going to receive a golden tribute in the form of a model.

Precisely at the hour agreed, the inner door opened and John Ericsson, a vigorous fifty-nine years of age, welcomed them in.

"Captain Ericsson all his life was careful of his personal appearance," a former drafting assistant remembered. "A close-fitting black frock surtout coat, well open at the front, with rolling collar, showing velvet vest and a good display of shirt front, a fine gold chain hung round the neck, looped at the first button-hole of the vest and attached to a watch carried in the fob of the vest. Usually light-colored, well-fitting trousers ...

"Expressive features, blue eyes, and brown, curly hair, fair complexion. His head was about medium size, his mouth well cut, upper lip a little drawn; the jaw large and firm-set, conveying an impression of firmness and individual character."[4]

"Having a thorough control of English expression...Ericsson was a most entertaining talker upon any subject that occupied his attention," wrote William C. Church, an editor who became his friend and biographer. "He was unusually fluent in speech, few men exceeding him in rapidity of utterance. ... Ericsson being a foreigner by birth, his thorough command of English, and his exact use of words and terms was a subject of remark."[5]

"He was the best talker I ever met..." said G.H. Robinson, who as the representative of the Delamater workshop regularly met with John Ericsson every Monday for many years. "His subject took full possession of him. His words came in torrents, gathering force as each new idea crowded for expression. It was not safe to interrupt, and rarely did one have the desire.

"He was not a tall man – measuring only five feet seven and one half inches," Robinson said. "He was stoutly built. His chest and shoulders showed the athlete. His head was large, every feature of his face was strong, particularly the mouth. His voice was powerful and he could thunder with it. Without being so, he gave one the impression that he was a large man."[6]

Like many another man of modest stature, John Ericsson was not shy. He once wrote that he considered himself "the person who has done more to promote marine engineering, mechanical motors, implements of naval warfare, etc., than any other ten persons together during the last third of the lifetime of the American republic."[7] Thus he would not have affected any embarrassment when the "representatives of the shipbuilding and industrial interests" advanced, processionlike, into his parlor bearing a 14-pound golden idol of the *Monitor* that had cost them $7,000, or twice the annual wage of the captain of a U.S. Navy warship, for example, the *U.S.S. Monitor*.[8]

Perhaps it was meant to be a reminder that not only pasteboard but gold had made the *Monitor* possible.

Ericsson had already had another memorable visit. Soon after the battle, the naval ministry of Sweden had asked Commodore Axel Adlersparre to go to New York and persuade his countryman to let Sweden use the *Monitor* designs for its defense. Adlersparre contacted Ericsson and expressed his fervent admiration in Swedish. Ericsson not only agreed to Sweden's request, but volunteered that "in the same moment that war is declared either by Sweden or against it, I shall return home to contribute my fortune, my strength and my life to the defense of my homeland."[9]

Perhaps the representatives of industry wanted to avert such a return, wanted their golden gift to forge a lifetime commitment, like a ring of gold.

In this, they succeeded entirely. John Ericsson did not return to his wife Amelia in London (nor, after two unsuccessful tries, did she join him again in America). He did not return to his native country, Sweden, even when his brother Nils invited him home, proposing a sentimental journey to their birthplace that might, since both were now famous, turn into a triumph. "I have a whole fleet to construct before I can take any rest," he wrote back.[10] John Ericsson did not return to Sweden even to see his son, Hjalmar.

Hjalmar was not Amelia's son, but Carolina's, conceived and born out of wedlock in Sweden before Ericsson left for England. It had been Nils who brought the abandoned child to Brita Sofia, his and John's own mother, who fostered Hjalmar and gave him a name; it was Nils who supported John's son, educating him as an engineer, finding him a job, first, in his own projects of building Sweden's canals and then, when Nils was entrusted with leading the creation of the new national railway system, bringing Hjalmar along. When Hjalmar Elworth demonstrated real talents, Nils brought him on into a leadership position. It was Nils who, at long intervals, reported to John Ericsson on Hjalmar's steady progress. Curiously, he had told his protegé that he was never to write to his father until his father first wrote to him.

Perhaps because it was already 38 years too late, John Ericsson did not return to Sweden to meet his son Hjalmar, to whom he had never written a letter nor ever spoken a word.

He was committed. He would remain in the United States of America, in the city of New York, and in a strange, signal loneliness for the last 27 years that he would live. (Yet the life he had abandoned proceeded on its course toward an eventual meeting here, in America.)

He was committed. The "Battery Associates" (and he was one of them) had a contract with the U.S. Government to build ten more Monitors, and larger ones were already under study for later construction. John Ericsson, who entrusted no one else with his designs, would have to stand at his drafting table for a long time to come.

"I want fame," he had written to Rowland, only months before the *Monitor*'s first battle. Now he had fame, and tribute, and the prospect of a fortune. But how could he have foreseen that his fame would become a life sentence of hard labor in exile?

He had been sentenced before.

In 1832, in London, England, John Ericsson had been arrested and taken to Kings Bench Prison for debts totaling £14,750.[11] He had accumulated this staggering indebtedness in the six years since he came to England from Sweden in 1826, on a year's leave from the Swedish army, using borrowed money. England's then ongoing industrial boom had brought him there. He had brought a working model of an invention that he thought would find a readier market in England, an engine that used heated air instead of steam for its motive medium. Though it did not prove practical, he went on to build and test designs for three steam locomotives, a machine to extract salt from seawater, and a steam turbine. England's expanding economy had created a group of speculators who would back any new thing, whether they understood its workings or not. If, as often happened during Ericsson's unlucky 13 years in England, he found a brilliant mechanical solution no one was yet ready to pay for, these speculators unfortunately could seek the law's redress.

Warned of impending arrest, he had written home to Sweden to Nils, his older brother, to Brita Sofia, his aged mother, and to Adolf von Rosen, his closest friend and sometime business partner.

Four months passed without an answer. At last a letter came from von Rosen that showed his friend knew nothing of his predicament.

He could not endure prison any longer, Ericsson wrote in reply. "I have often been at wit's end how to meet my daily needs." The prison had a barred window to the street where truly indigent prisoners were allowed to beg from passersby. In his despair, Ericsson felt himself slipping into a deadly sloth and apathy. He was even considering bankruptcy, which would mean giving up all his patents. Yet declaring bankruptcy entailed legal costs he could not pay. "I have enclosed a letter to Nils," he told von Rosen, "be so kind as to forward it soon, I am very much worried that my mother is anxious about me."[12]

But he was still in prison two months later, in November 1832, when a visitor was escorted to the door of his cell. It was Nils.

The desperate faction of John's mind leaped up with hope and embraced his brother with joy. But there was another faction that held him motionless in the dark.

They were brothers, Nils just a year older. Long before, in the village of their birth, both had seen the hammer fall and fall, they had glimpsed the abyss and been twinned in dread.

But their temperaments were quite unlike. "John, who was daring to an extreme, especially strove for physical strength. Nils, on the other hand, was very anxious all his life to be well-regarded and, in his younger days, especially anxious to guard his natural good looks...he was especially attentive to his superiors and outstandingly cooperative, dependable and punctual..."[13] *Dependable, punctual.* Brita Sofia's influence on Nils was evident; her family had some social pretensions, before her husband Olof lost everything. She knew how gentlefolk behaved. But John showed the influence of Olof, who in bad times had plunged on a silver mine, who ended up making his living by making explosions. If Nils was a steady flame, John blazed and sparked powerfully but with intermittency.

Isn't it a dangerous path he has taken? Nils wrote to ask their mutual friend, Adolf von Rosen, soon after John left Sweden for England. Later Nils sounded a hopeful note: *Should John's fortunes take a happy turn ... we all know the part you have played in his progress.* But Nils wrote more ominously the following year: "Worried, I have read through John's letter several times, his situation is perilous, may everything come out successfully." Elsewhere he writes that "my hope that John will be able to straighten things out is beginning to fade." And in another letter, before he learned that John was actually in King's Bench Prison: "I would have been glad to make a trip to England this fall, if only I had known how John's affairs stood and whether he could help in any way to make the trip less costly."[14]

Here Nils stood in the dim corridor of King's Bench Prison, outside John's dark cell. John looked at him through the door, well-dressed, well-barbered, smiling but beginning to show impatience. Impatience, not anger. Just possibly Nils was secretly pleased that his direst expectations had been validated, just possibly he had come to gloat. John beckoned, and Nils bent to enter the low door.

Nils was the first among John Ericsson's many creditors.

When John Ericsson left Sweden in 1826 for a year in England, Brita Sofia had a small income as proprietor of the Göta Canal headquarters canteen (and, most profitably, the licensed brewer of strong spirits served there). But one year had now stretched out to six and the canteen was a thing of the past and Nils Ericsson was the sole support of mother and sister, besides planning to marry early the next year.

Obviously, John Ericsson was in no financial condition to help Nils with the expenses of his son (though many years later, when Nils asked for reimbursement for his various outlays on Hjalmar's behalf, John responded with alacrity). John's son had been born in 1824 to Carolina Lilliesköld, the daughter of his landlord. He had proposed marriage but been rejected by her parents, who may also have forced her to give the newborn Hjalmar to a farmer. Or, just possibly, John himself did so. But she regretted having done it and wrote to Brita Sofia. Nils is thought to have located the boy and brought him to Brita Sofia. She is said to have treated little Hjalmar as her own. Nevertheless, Brita Sofia replaced Ericsson as his surname with a combination of E and L, the initial letters of his parents' family names, plus "worth," inspired by a novel of Sir Walter Scott she was reading, *Kenilworth.* So although Hjalmar would grow up among Nils Ericsson's own sons John, Carl and Werner, a unique and separate Elworth he became.

But then, Nils, too, would later make his own surname unique and separate, angering his brother John.

Now Nils straightened up, glanced around the tiny grimy cell lit by a single guttering candle, and looked back at his brother with a gratifying sympathy. He had come to see what could be done, he said.

It must have been true. He remained in London for more than a month. It was first necessary to help John, who all his life hardly used any financial system but his check stubs, to get some order into his myriad obligations and his few assets. Nils negotiated on John's behalf with the most vindictive of the creditors, as well as with the English prison authorities. Nils exerted the organizing talent and powers of persuasion that he would come to apply to driving the establishment of vast new public works in Sweden, qualities that would eventually earn extraordinary recognition from the Swedish state: a title of nobility and the largest retirement pension ever awarded an individual.

By the time Nils left London, his brother was again a free man.

"Our previous pleasant relationship is restored," John wrote to von Rosen about his brother Nils' efforts.[15]

Whether it was because of Nils' advice or his example, John seems now to have reconsidered his way of life. After another, briefer confinement, again for debt, in Fleet Prison in 1835 that he was able to handle without Nils' help, John took a job with the new Eastern Counties Railway[16] to gain a dependable income, hoping to continue his inventing after-hours. He also married and with his wife Amelia set up a household on Trafalgar Street. After so much turmoil, his prospects seemed to brighten.

But he was an inventor, not a railroad man. The after-hours lengthened and eventually pushed his daytime duties aside. He invented, among a surprising number of new things, the first effective marine propulsion screw.

An American friend introduced him to a visiting American naval officer who proved enthusiastic about the screw and its application. He invested in Ericsson's proposal to design a warship in which an improved steam engine would drive a horizontal shaft to a submerged screw aft. This would eliminate the vulnerable paddle-wheels that made Fulton's steamships militarily useless.

In 1839, encouraged by this same investor to think that he had obtained the U.S. Navy's approval for the proposed design, Ericsson took passage for America, leaving his wife in London. The inventor anticipated an intensive assignment and then a swift return to England. But it was five more years before Ericsson's remarkable screw-driven steam warship, *U.S.S. Princeton*, was launched, to an acclaim that promised fame for Ericsson.

Yet within days of this triumph a tragic accident aboard the *Princeton* would snatch away these glowing prospects and once more test John Ericsson's resolve.

NOTES

1. Church, William C., 1906, i, 294.
2. Still, William N., 1988, 14-15, 18-24.

3. West, Richard S., Jr., 1957, 99-129.
4. Church, 1906, i, 112-13.
5. Church, 1906, i, 224, 223.
6. Robinson, G.H. 1894. Robinson and Bushnell were executors of Ericsson's estate.
7. Ericsson, John to Axel Adlersparre, 1876, in Church, 1907, ii, 183.
8. Randel, William P., 1969, 279.
9. Ericsson, John to Axel Adlersparre, June 6, 1862 in Goldkuhl, Carola, 1961, 187.
10. Goldkuhl, Carola, 1961, 179.
11. Lindwall, Gustaf, 1937, 116.
12. *Ibid.*, 120-21
13. Goldkuhl, Carola, 1966, 83.
14. Ericson, Nils to Adolf von Rosen, various dates between 1826 and 1832, in Goldkuhl, Carola, 1966, 83-9.
15. Lindwall, 1937, 130
16. *Ibid.*, 151.

CHAPTER 2

Captain Ericsson, the most extraordinary mechanical genius of the present day!

It was all he could have wished, to hear this on the deck of his new ship *Princeton*, returning to New York harbor in triumph.

It was October 19, 1843, only eight years after London's Fleet Prison, eleven years since Nils' providential visit had freed him from King's Bench Prison.

Beside John Ericsson on the deck of the *U.S.S. Princeton* stood Francis Barber Ogden. Now the American consul in Bristol, England, he had been among the first to invest in Ericsson's inventions. Through many of the Swedish immigrant's vicissitudes, the American had stood by him; months before, when the *Princeton* was being built, Ericsson had written urging him to come and join him on this "pinnacle of honor and renown."[1] To accept this invitation had cost Ogden a lot, taking leave from his official duties in England, making a fortnight's voyage across the Atlantic Ocean; but now, with characteristic generosity, he told Ericsson he was repaid.

...the most extraordinary mechanical genius of the present day!

Robert Stockton's voice rang out over the throng on the deck. A captain in the U.S. Navy, he was commander of the *Princeton.* He thrust his brimming glass skyward and "hundreds of respectable gentlemen" joined him in the toast.[2] They drank to Ericsson, to the *Princeton,* and to the victory this new kind of warship had won for the United States today. Not a martial exploit, although after today there was no doubt of such victories in the future, but instead a victory in peaceable contest, a race that humiliated their old rival, so recently a foe, England, whose fastest ocean steamer, the *Great Western,* had today been bested without firing a shot.[3]

For Captain Robert Stockton, USN, it was also a day of triumph. He had seen the need and possibility of a steam-powered propeller warship when others in the naval profession had been united in its scorn. He had overcome such prejudices to secure government support for Ericsson's experimental warship. Stockton had ventured his reputation and some of his own funds on making this warship a reality.

But it was Ogden who had brought the two together. That was six years before, in 1837, while he was American consul in Liverpool. Ogden was an able official, and he would continue in the consular service for the rest of his career, but his heart was elsewhere, like Ericsson's. Amidst his daily duties he kept hearing the siren call of invention.

The consul was a member of a prominent New Jersey family. His grandfather, Robert Ogden, had been elected to represent New Jersey at a meeting of the colonies in 1765; his father, Matthias, had fought under George Washington and become colonel of the 1st New Jersey regiment, then brigadier-general, and after the Revolution a member of the New Jersey legislative council and a presidential elector.

Francis Ogden had shown an early interest in mechanics, and specifically the steam engine; it is thought he knew Robert Fulton well.

When the year 1812 brought war, Francis Ogden entered the army and during his three-year service was an aide-de-camp under General Andrew Jackson. In 1817 he went to England, where he designed and built steamboat engines with unique features that were praised by the great James Watt himself.

In 1830, the year after Jackson became president, Ogden was appointed United States consul in Liverpool. His interest in steam power did not wane, and he seems to have invested a substantial amount in John Ericsson's inventions as early as 1831.Through Ogden, Ericsson had obtained a patent for a steam engine improvement in that year, and six years later applied for an American patent on his propeller. The consul was one of the investors who had shown understanding when Ericsson, after his imprisonment, had taken a regular job with a new railroad line. He knew that Ericsson had lost none of his enthusiasm for invention, and he continued to promote the Swede. The first boat equipped with Ericsson's screw propeller, a small steam vessel built for demonstration of the device, was named after Ogden.[4]

It was Adolf von Rosen, a Swedish associate of Ericsson's, who arranged for a party of Admiralty officials including the First Sea Lord, Sir Charles Adams, Sir William Symonds, and Sir William Parry, leader of several successful polar expeditions, to make an excursion on the Thames in the Admiralty's own barge, towed by the little *Francis B. Ogden*, a third of its size. Ericsson, anticipating orders, had laid out his drawings of the propeller boat on board the barge.

The gold-braid sailors arrived safely at Somerset House, but to the surprise and dismay of Ericsson and Ogden they gave the two only a dismissive thanks for the ride. Apparently the gold braids were convinced that a vessel driven by a propeller at the stern had to be unsteerable. Certainly it was easiest for them to believe that warships should continue to be fueled as they always had by the wind-power freely available everywhere.[5]

But Ogden did not give up. When Robert F. Stockton, whom the consul might have known back in New Jersey, turned up in England, Ogden arranged for him to go aboard the little *Ogden* for another demonstration trip down the Thames, this time to Greenwich.

Stockton's family was as prominent in New Jersey as Ogden's. His grandfather had signed the Declaration of Independence, his father had been a politically well-connected lawyer and official. When the War of 1812 began, Stockton had left school to join the Navy. He returned as something of a hero and took up his part in his family's canal-building project, the Delaware and Raritan Canal. Their wealth was deeply committed to the canal, which would eventually carry lucrative cargoes of Pennsylvania coal directly from Philadelphia through New Jersey to burgeoning New York City.

But in 1837 a wide-reaching financial crisis forced suspension of the canal work while Robert went abroad to look for additional funding. He retained his Navy officer's commission, so his travel took the form of a return to duty for as long as he found it convenient. England was one of his destinations,[6] and while there he called on Consul Ogden, who invited him to take a cruise on the Thames.

Stockton seems to have recognized immediately the advantages Ericsson's propeller would confer on driving and towing cargoes through narrow shallow canals where sidewheel steamboats could not go. "Ericsson, we will make your name ring on the Delaware as soon as we get your propeller there!" he cried, while they dined in a famous Greenwich tavern.[7]

They could have found a lot to talk about, though their canal experiences could hardly have been more different. Ericsson's father, Olof, had been foreman of the blasting crew on the Göta Canal, Sweden's project to unite the North Sea with the Baltic by a ship canal right across the nation. Ericsson had worked on the canal all through his teens, much of the time at the bottom of the huge excavation as a "leveler"' whose job it was to keep the digging of 600 sweating workmen straight and true. Stockton had seen plenty of canal building, too, but from the top down.[8]

At table, Ogden may well have thought Ericsson and Stockton complemented each other perfectly. Stockton was a financier who had skillfully lobbied the New Jersey state legislature for a remarkably advantageous canal franchise; though he was probably a quick study in canal technology, he had not personally designed or built anything. Ericsson, on the other hand, had proved thoroughly unsuccessful at the politics of innovation; as Ogden well knew, the inventor had more than once managed to turn backers of his mechanical projects into vengeful creditors who got him locked up in debtor's prison. It was the forms and forces of machines he knew how to manipulate, not the levers of interest and advantage. Both were specialists, and had neither made any pretension to the expertise of the other, their story would have had a different ending.

But the beginning seemed full of promise. Before leaving for New Jersey, Stockton hired Ericsson to design a small propeller vessel to tow canal barges. It would be built under Ericsson's supervision in England.

In January of the following year, 1839, Stockton returned to England to see the launching of the *Robert F. Stockton*, his canal steamer. It was probably at this time Stockton and Ericsson discussed applying the Swede's inventions to a warship.

The idea of a steam-driven warship was not new. Fulton had already designed two military sidewheelers, one of which exploded with great loss of life and the other proved unusable for naval purposes. The sidewheels and their high geared-drive mechanism were vulnerable to cannon fire, and this seemed to rule out further development of steam for military combat use. But Ericsson's submerged propeller would overcome this vulnerability and by bringing steam power directly to it, Ericsson had eliminated the gearing as well. From one end to the other, Ericsson's propulsion system could be shielded by water from enemy bombardment. Stockton would claim that the idea of this system was his, and Ericsson only the "ingenious mechanic" who carried it out. But that was eventful years later.

Before he left for America again, Stockton paid Ericsson to prepare "a model of a war screw-steamer of two thousand tons, with a set of detailed drawing plans." He told Ericsson that he would have no trouble getting the U.S. Navy to sponsor the project: "'I will let you have...the finest frigate in the American Navy' – meaning," Ericsson wrote von Rosen, "to try the propeller on."[9] Exciting. But quite an undertaking for a full- time employee of the Eastern Counties Railway to carry out in his spare time.

Ericsson's duties as chief engineer only began with designing new mechanical equipment and traveling out to inspect new track ("The number of things on our railway that I have undertaken to do drives me crazy.")[10] His capacity for work was phenomenal, but his letters to von Rosen more and more often bore the return address of the railroad office, where he worked on Stockton's ship proposal, and on drawings of a new file-cutting machine he had recently invented, late into the night.

Amelia, his wife, felt abandoned and let him know it. "She is jealous of everything, even of my machines," Ericsson complained.

He had first seen Amelia in her childhood when a businessman named Charles Seidler, whom he met soon after arriving in England, invited him home. Mrs. Seidler's half-sister lived with them, Amelia, age 10 and pretty, bright and musical. The Swede and his hosts formed an enduring friendship and for the next nine years he was an increasingly fascinated spectator as Amelia ripened into a beauty courted by many.

Among these was "the handsomest man in London," an aristocrat to whom she bore a daughter, Ady, though he was married to an invalid wife.

John Ericsson intervened. "No other woman on earth has so bewitched me," he would explain later.[11] But he might also have coveted the role of rescuer, even stepfather. By now he would have heard through letters or the Swedish papers that Carolina Lilliesköld, back in Sweden, had married a prominent professor named Schlyter the year before. Through his brother Nils he heard that his son Hjalmar, now 14 years old, was following in his footsteps with a summer job on Nils' latest canal project. Yet John had nothing to send Hjalmar as encouragement but words, words for a child to whom he had never spoken. Maybe he felt Amelia and her Ady offered him a second chance.

In October, 1836, at St. John's Church in London, John Ericsson, 33, and Amelia Byam, 19, were married.

It was not long until he discovered he had no patience with parenting. Much later, he wrote his brother that Amelia had broken a promise when they married that they would not have custody of her illegitimate daughter.[12] Yet young Amelia was deeply invested in her child. Before long both her husband's absences and his impatience with Ady became inflamed issues between them.

Discord at home, overload at work and Stockton's assignment keeping him at his drawing table every night exhausted him, and he began to feel a quite uncharacteristic guilt toward the main source of his and Amelia's support.

"If I were to do my duty to the railway, I would immediately move out into the country along the right of way and say goodbye forever to my mechanical devices and to my vital contacts with the workshops and their people ...To tell you the truth I am ashamed of the neglect I have shown the Company."[13] Yet the design of a new kind of warship for the Americans seems to open a whole new dimension to John Ericsson, a new world of possibilities.

He writes to Robert F. Stockton suggesting that he visit New York. To his surprise, the American writes back urgently dissuading him, saying that unexpectedly he has found the Navy's leadership wholly opposed to their warship project.

This is not the first time travel to America has crossed his mind. Back in 1826 Ericsson had written his Swedish friend and backer Gussander that he would return to Sweden either in a year or never – preferring "hotter air" on "the other side of the globe" to returning home without fame.[14]

Now, on October 3, 1839, with 13 years of unsuccess in England behind him, he writes von Rosen: "My planned trip to America is a secret and if it comes about I am most likely to go on the British Queen on the 30th of this month." On the 15th he writes that "the British Queen is expected every moment... I have quite made up my mind to set out for New York by this vessel..." And on the day before his departure he writes a letter in which, facing the uncertainties of an ocean crossing, he conveys to his best friend and partner von Rosen a contingent bequest of all European rights in his inventions, with half the profits to be used to liquidate certain of their joint business debts and then the remainder to support Ericsson's "widow or child."[15] He leaves for America alone.

NOTES

1. Ericsson, John to Francis B. Ogden, 1844, quoted in Ogden to Adolf von Rosen July 1844, in Lindwall, Gustaf, 1937, 199.
2. Ericsson to John O. Sargent, 1845, in Church, William C., 1906, 118.
3. *New York Sunday Mercury*, Oct. 22, 1843, 2: "Race on the Ocean."
4. Church, 1906, i, 91-4.
5. Goldkuhl, Carola, 1961, 86-7 and Lindwall, Gustaf, 1937, 142-5.
6. Bayard, Samuel J., 1856, 10-12, 65-6, 76-7.
7. Church, 1906, i, 93.
8. Lindwall, 1937, 152.
9. Ericsson to John O. Sargent, Jan. 24, 1845, in Church, 1906, i, 107.
10. Ericsson to von Rosen, 1839, in Goldkuhl, 1961, 83.
11. Anna Eckhill to Elias Grip, October 9, 1919. Eckhill, a descendant of Ericsson's sister Anna Carolina, replied in this lengthy account to an inquiry from an Ericsson biographer.
12. Ericsson to Nils Ericson, December 1867, in Runvik, Margaretha, 1996, 61.
13. Ericsson to von Rosen, 1839, in Goldkuhl, 1961, 83.
14. Ericsson to A.F. Gussander, Nov. 26, 1826, in Lindwall, 1937, 68.
15. Ericsson to Adolf von Rosen, dates cited, in Lindwall, op. 1937, 176-7.

CHAPTER 3

"I am very pleased with America – the people here are much better than the travel writers say," Ericsson wrote to von Rosen, soon after his arrival in New York on November 23, 1839. "The air is fresh and clean – I feel better than ever. The traces of rheumatism have left me entirely and as for my ability to concentrate I note a remarkable improvement since I have been able to put aside the English meat diet. I think I must have been a blockhead when I left old Albion."

He writes about his plans. What he describes is the schedule of a visit, or a series of visits, not of an emigration. "I have inspected almost all the Factories in the city, and next week I will look at the rest, to decide which parts can be made here in this country (I mean of the machinery for the planned frigate). Then I will get started on the working drawings, and when I have everything here under way I will go over to England (probably in February) to get the remainder made, and around next June I will be coming back here to install the machinery, and in the fall, to launch the ship."[1]

His optimism seemed warranted. To his surprise, when he arrived in New York Robert Stockton received him amicably, saying that the prospects for building the frigate had improved. More detailed drawings of the vessel had been asked for, he said. Encouraged and trusting, Ericsson set to work.

Several months later, he had another surprise, to which he responded with equal optimism. In May, 1840, Amelia arrived in New York. "Amelia's arrival here on the *British Queen* was not only a very pleasant surprise, but at the same time one of the more fortunate events I have met with," he wrote his friend von Rosen, in whom he had confided his marital problems, and who is thought to have helped Amelia to follow her husband. Ericsson writes that before she came, he had felt the onset of an apathy "that I think might have ended soon in a tragic scene...

"Through the magnifying glass of my imagination, Amelia's many small flaws had taken on giant shapes, so that my letters to her not only lacked in love, they did not even breathe a friendly spirit – actually I tried to convince myself that I hated her, but this made me quite unhappy – her arrival in the midst of all this, forlorn and humiliated, freely admitting her unfairness toward me, with the tenderest promises of her future conduct, could not but bring a happy alteration in my mood and disposition...

"Amelia is now a new person, and we are happy in the full meaning of the word."[2]

But Amelia's coming compounded the difficulties of an imposture into which he had fallen. He wanted his clients to think of him as well off and therefore not dependent on his patent license income. Later this would lead him to make the license fees for the many inventions he incorporated into Stockton's war frigate contingent on the vessel's successful performance, a gesture for which he would pay dearly.[3] But now he was trying to keep up a certain style that, even alone, he had hardly been able to afford.

News of his supposed high life even reached Sweden, prompting his mother to write him, in September 1840, reproving his extravagance.

"What Mamma says about my life is based on falsehoods, apparently spread by a Baron Duben," Ericsson wrote back. "I left England with a promise to Amelia to return in three months' time – I did not keep my promise – which is why, without consulting me, she set out across the Atlantic Ocean and arrived here in May of this year.

"It appears that Baron Duben does not understand that, in the real world, people may live in fine houses and wear nice clothes, while starving. That I have learned this from my own experience I hardly care about, but that my wife has suffered this for many long weeks and months truly grieves me, especially when she is condemned even by my mother. It seems to be the fashion among my friends to consider Amelia and me extravagant because we have always made a good outward show – among other things, my wife's clothing has attracted comments – but she is thrifty to an extreme – we were out evening before last and as usual she attracted a lot of attention – she was wearing a black dress I had given her in 1837."

Brita Sofia may not have written solely to reprove her son's excesses. She was worried about his son Hjalmar. Nils, now the head of an ambitious new Swedish canal- building project, had given 14-year-old Hjalmar an assignment – the very same job both he and John had learned to perform, many years before, the "leveler" who with a transit and a map covered with calculations keeps a large digging crew headed in the right direction. Brita Sofia may have felt that the boy would find it too difficult.

"Your picture of my Son's critical situation is exaggerated," John responds. "Difficulty (this young man has not yet encountered adversity) is healthful for the development of a man's character. Entering the world too early is harmful, and under 20 years of age one is always young enough to learn. To practice practical skills, the kinds that Hjalmar gains daily as a Leveler, and to develop his physique, before he sets out on the completion of his studies, I think highly beneficial for a man.

"Rest assured, Mamma, about my Brother's expenses for the young fellow, they should be repaid before Nils has any use for them. The money for Hjalmar's impending needs I shall send soon."[4]

These confident promises of reimbursement and support are uneasy neighbors, in Ericsson's letter, with his discussion of starving in a fine house. Doubtless these pretensions took their toll. Amelia also found the New York summer heat very hard to bear. She missed old friends and her family back in London, and most of all she missed her daughter Ady.

In October, 1840, Ericsson told von Rosen that after five months in America "Amelia is now going back on the *British Queen*. Do not think we are displeased with one another, on the contrary, our time together has been an unbroken link of happiness and friendship. I am going to do my best to go to England during the winter to place the plans before the English government and it is best that Amelia return during the best traveling season. Expenses here, with a wife, are completely unreasonable. Many have also imagined that I intend to settle here -- this works against me and is now reason enough to send Amelia home. Also, she hates this country and longs very much to see Ady, to which I cannot object; summing up, I wish Amelia to travel home – I have much to do and she is a constraint."[5]

Stockton had ordered from him new, more detailed drawings of their steam propeller warship for the Navy. With Amelia safely on the high seas, Ericsson returned to his usual 18-hour-a-day working schedule and completed the package.

But when these new drawings had been delivered, "Stockton behaved badly" he wrote to von Rosen. "I see that he wants to get rid of me, drive me out of the country, now that he has my working drawings in his hands. *He never meant for me to be here during the actual construction -- the man is cold, ambitious, cunning and miserly* ...a really handsome character, you see."[6]

Yet even Ericsson's new drawings did not budge the Navy Department. The frigate project was becalmed.

John Ericsson had begun to realize that the American officer's problem in finding support for the frigate project was political. Despite being a Navy officer Stockton had become prominent in the election campaign of William Henry Harrison, who was running against the incumbent President Van Buren.

Ericsson seems to have decided that he could do without Stockton, and might be better able to represent himself. The Swedish visitor decided to go to Washington. It was a bold decision for a non-citizen[7] a newcomer to American politics, indeed, to America. He had been in the States for hardly a year. Yet the outcome of the trip was encouraging, as he related to von Rosen:

"Ten days ago I returned from Washington, where I had gone to contact the leadership directly. The Secretary of War, Mr. Poinsett, to whom I presented a drawing of the gunboat in connection with his plans for coastal defense, was especially gracious to me. My drawing (the new engine with the propeller as the means of propulsion) was approved in every respect and I am able to give you the happy news that it is going to be presented to Congress as soon as its session begins in December – this is going to be a tough nut to crack for that scoundrel Stockton – for that is what I find him to be, basically...

"The Secretary of the Navy, Mr. Paulding...told me right out: 'We have the highest opinion of your new propeller and think its introduction in the Navy of the greatest importance, but we cannot...approve...such [a] large scale as proposed by Capt. Stockton...'

"By the assurances I received I am convinced that an appropriation will be made for the matter this winter, whether that bastard Stockton is in the picture or not."[8] But he realized, he wrote, that these prospects depended entirely on the reelection of President Van Buren, and with it Poinsett's and Paulding's continuance at the head of their departments. If the incumbent lost, his own cause might be lost. He must have understood that his flanking maneuver would eventually come to the knowledge of Robert F. Stockton.

Van Buren was defeated and William Henry Harrison was elected president, but he died of pneumonia a month after the election. Vice President John Tyler, who happened to be a friend of Robert F. Stockton, assumed the executive office. Ericsson, realizing that he had chosen the losing side, may well have despaired of the U.S. Navy project into which he had invested so much labor. Yet he had also come to the States for another purpose, to promote the use of his propeller, on which he had an American patent. On this he had barely begun.

Ericsson summarized his next moves in an account he sent John O. Sargent some years later:

"Stockton's inability to do anything with the Navy induced me at once to turn round and see what could be effected with private individuals. The result was the fitting out of the *Clarion*, the *Vandalia,* on the lakes, the steamboats *Propeller* and *Ericsson* and a barge for the Canadian government, all of them running on the St. Lawrence."[9] Thus Ericsson, with his patented propeller, began to eke out a living and to gain a certain recognition from American engineers.

Perhaps it was this modest progress that encouraged him to write von Rosen about his plans for Hjalmar, his son. "I can now give Nils such proof about the propeller that he can take on the responsibility for its introduction in the canals back home – and thus do something for my boy, whose education now requires a substantial investment. ... If I can find the money he will later be educated for the Artillery and the

Surveyor Corps – and finally, when he has learned as an officer to *obey* , I am going to make him into an engineer, if he has the head for it, of which I have no doubt."[10]

John Ericsson had also begun to miss his wife. Now he wrote to Amelia asking her to come back. This time, though, she refused, saying that she could not leave Ady. Ericsson again appealed to von Rosen for help, and near the end of the summer she returned to New York.

"My wife's coming here was a blessing," Ericsson wrote his old friend. "She is much improved, or I should say, just as I have so often wished her to be."[11]

But a new threat to their marital peace appeared, in an unexpected shape. Early in October, 1841, Ericsson received a message from Stockton telling him that the warship project had at last received Navy approval and summoning him to Princeton, New Jersey.[12]

They met amicably. Stockton probably said nothing about Ericsson's meddling in Washington. At this critical juncture he needed the inventor and, being a well-practiced politician, he was adept at hiding his feelings. He told Ericsson what was needed: more drawings to new dimensions, "cost of hull, equipments, etc., etc., as well as for the engines, displacement, metacentre, centre of gravity, centre of flotation... etc." The inventor was able to set to work on a steam-driven propeller warship for the United States Navy at last.

Samuel Risley, who became his assistant at this time, reminisced: "During the period I was with him he accomplished an immense amount of work. He would work out designs in pencil and I would make fresh drawings from them in detail. He gave up this practice, he informed me, after I left him and gave particular attention to all details, working out every screw in finished drawings. He said he profited by it in the end. ...As a rule he spent about fourteen hours a day at his drawing-board.

"In designing he was marvelously quick, and with his scale and a pencil he would sketch almost equal to a finished drawing. He had been thoroughly grounded in Euclid and his conceptions of mechanical movements were clear and distinct. He had great method and order in laying out his work and its continuance after was easy to him – more, in fact, a pleasure than a labor."[13]

William C. Church, in the authorized biography, sums up Ericsson's key contributions to the *Princeton:*

"Altogether one hundred and twenty-four working drawings were furnished by Ericsson, occupying, with the sketches, skeleton plans, and diagrams necessary in their construction, two hundred and seven days of the time of a man who could do in one day double the work of an ordinary draughtsman; one hundred and thirteen days were devoted to actual superintendence at New York and Philadelphia, and in traveling to and fro... The manufacturers of the machinery, guns, gun-carriages, etc., testified that they did their work from Ericsson's drawings and under his directions... This was but part of the labor to which Ericsson gave two of the best years of his life."[14]

Long before Ericsson had completed these two years of work on the *Princeton*, had given hour after hour to the labors and pleasures of his drawing table and had spent days in travel to personally superintend fabricators, Amelia, who "could be jealous of a steam engine," had given up on their marriage and returned to London for the last time.

They would continue to correspond until her death in July 1867, and he would continue to support her as his wife, but they would never see one another again. After Amelia's death, John would write to his brother Nils:

"My success and happiness in the world required that I would not be troubled with a wife and children who had every right to live with me. Fate, through this misalliance, put me in the way of giving 25 years' undivided, undisturbed time to my profession, and I thank Heaven for that..."[15]

But that success and happiness still lay far ahead.

In 1840, in his impatience with and possibly ignorance of the American system, Ericsson had made bold to pull strings and tamper with levers whose mechanism was beyond his ken. Robert Stockton, who would later represent his state in the U.S. Senate, must have regarded Ericsson's excursion to Washington as nothing less than treachery, but he nursed his grudge in silence.

However, when Stockton realized that the single most conspicuous feature of the new warship, its biggest gun, was about to be still another Ericsson invention, the "Orator," which Ericsson had brought along with him from England, the politician convinced himself he could design an even bigger gun of even greater power. "He had one forged...and sent it to the Phoenix Foundry, New York, to be bored and finished under Ericsson's directions," Church records. "It was of the same calibre as the imported gun...but a foot more in diameter at the breech, and much heavier. This Stockton gun was considered at the time to be a remarkable specimen of workmanship and great confidence was placed in its strength, because of the supposed superior quality of American iron."[16]

Stockton, seeing his dream warship materialize, seemed to express great appreciation. At a festive dinner on the evening of September 7, 1843, after witnessing the launching of the *U.S.S. Princeton* , Captain Stockton told Mayor John Lowry of Princeton, New Jersey that he had "been all over the world in search of a man who could invent or carry out what he thought was necessary to make a complete ship of war." He paused to let that sink in, glancing around the table at the admiring faces of Recorder William Rodgers and Aldermen Van Deventer and Knighton, and Assistants Clow, Paxson, Suydam, Stryker, and Craig. He had "at last found that man," Stockton continued. "He is my friend here by my side, Captain Ericsson," and he asked his guests, all the governing officials of his home town, to drink the inventor's health "with three times three."[17]

Yet Ericsson may have glanced up at his backer in surprise at this speech, hearing that Stockton had brought the idea of a steam propeller warship to England full-grown, when he remembered being present at its birth on the Thames.

And Stockton made sure that his massive "Peacemaker" was mounted forward while Ericsson's "Orator" was moved aft, doubtless to remind the inventor who came first in the *Princeton* project.

There was no doubt which of them was the skillful promoter. Stockton took his new ship to New York, perhaps on a shakedown cruise but also to demonstrate her great speed in a memorable way. *Great Western*, first among the side-wheel steamers making regular crossings with passengers and cargo, was reputed to be England's fastest. It was not coincidental that *Princeton* was in New York harbor on October 19, 1843, the day when England's pride left the dock for a return voyage. *Princeton* raced her, left her astern, in fact ran rings around her.[18]

Ericsson, the most extraordinary mechanical genius of the present day![19]

It was all John Ericsson could have wished, to hear this on the deck of his new ship *Princeton*. It was only eight years after his last experience of an English debtor's prison.

...the most extraordinary mechanical genius of the present day!

The inventor and the commander, the short but powerfully built Swedish immigrant and the tall, lean naval officer who wore his gold epaulets as if born to them, stood side by side with Francis Ogden, the consul who had brought them together as the *Princeton,* the first screw-propelled steam warship ever built, swiftly sheared the waves back into New York Harbor.

NOTES

1. Lindwall, Gustaf, 1937, 181-2.
2. Lindwall, 1937, 211-12.
3. Church, William C., 1906, i, 119-20, 145-7.
4. Ericsson, John to Brita Sofia Ericsson, Oct., 1840, in Goldkuhl, 1961, 79-80.

5. Ericsson to Adolf von Rosen, Oct. 1, 1840, in Lindwall, 212-13.
6. Ericsson to von Rosen, May 31, 1840, in Lindwall, 185.
7. He would become an American citizen in 1848.
8. Ericsson to von Rosen, Oct., 1840, in Lindwall, 187.
9. Ericsson to John O. Sargent, Jan. 24, 1845, in Church, 1906, i, 107-8.
10. Ericsson to von Rosen, Nov. 22, 1841.
11. Ericsson to von Rosen, 1842 in Lindwall, 217.
12. Stockton, Robert F. to Ericsson Oct. 2, 1840, in Church, 1906, i, 121.
13. Risley, Samuel to William C. Church, in Church, 1906, i, 112-115.
14. Church, 1906, i, 122.
15. Ericsson to Nils Ericson, Dec. 1867, in Goldkuhl, 1961, 77.
16. Church, 1906, i, 124.
17. Ericsson to John O. Sargent, Jan. 24, 1845 in Church, 1906, i, 118; and personal communication Feb. 6, 2002 from Tad Bennicoff, Special Collections Assistant, Seeley G. Mudd Manuscript Library, Princeton University, of the Borough of Princeton NJ Historical Subject File document, undated, including page 2 addendum on "special meeting of Council held on the morning of September 5, 1843..."
18. Church, 1906, i, 135.
19. Church, 1906, i, 118.

CHAPTER 4

Bearing such laurels, *Princeton* was now ready for presentation to Stockton's real public, the one that counted most for an aspiring politician. President John Tyler had heard about the project, he had encouraged his friend Robert Stockton to proceed with it, and now the noble ship had been the means to embarrass old foe England. It was the right moment to bring *Princeton* to Washington, to invite the president and Congress for a cruise on the Potomac.

Ericsson, hearing of these plans, naturally assumed that he, as the only man capable of "inventing or carrying out...what was necessary for a complete ship of war," "the most extraordinary mechanical genius of the present day" would be part of the ultimate festivity in Washington.

After all, Ericsson had invented the improved steam engine, its direct coupling to the propeller, and the efficient propeller, all of which made possible placing the propulsion system below the direct impact of enemy fire. For his powerful "Orator" 12-inch cannon he had invented a gun carriage that could handle the violent recoil, and a device to fire cannons just at the moment when the ship reached the horizontal plane, improving their accuracy. These and many other Ericsson inventions led Stockton to report to the Navy, without naming their inventor, that he believed "this small ship will be able to battle with any vessel, however large, if she is not invincible against any foe. The improvements in the art of war, adopted on board the *Princeton*, may be productive of more important results than anything that has occurred since the invention of gunpowder."

Stockton also told the Navy that his ship had "by far the most formidable guns afloat, able to 'throw a greater weight of metal than most frigates, with a certainty heretofore unknown...'"[1] What Stockton did not tell the Navy was that his "Peacemaker" was not reinforced around the breech with iron bands as Ericsson's "Orator" was, nor had it been as thoroughly tested.

The president and the congressmen set a date in February.

Ericsson said to Stockton that he would be waiting at Wall Street dock to join the triumphant tour southward. He felt, with merit, that the congratulations of the president and the congressmen were not Stockton's alone. Stockton's reply to this information has not been recorded, but under his breath he may well have muttered "You have already had your visit to Washington."

On the morning of the ship's departure the inventor arrived at the dock, carrying his valise, in good time. With excited anticipation he watched his gallant ship approach. But with astonishment that turned to dismay and then fury, he saw her pass and continue out of sight without so much as a salute.

Who knows? Perhaps, without meaning to, Stockton had saved the inventor's life. But John Ericsson would spend the rest of his life trying to regain his well-deserved passage on the *U.S.S. Princeton.*

A peculiar spectacle: a graceful new frigate glides down the Potomac River below Washington in the sunshine of an early spring day, through water roiled by breezes that find no sails at all stretched on its three tall masts. The steady vibration that powers its progress is bested continually by the hum of conversation and laughter from a large gathering on its deck. Yet from time to time the conversation is interrupted by a shattering roar that echoes between the low densely wooded banks. After each roar, delighted exclamations, mock declarations of war against an unseen foe, and toasts: "Fifty-four forty or fight!" "Oregon, the Peacemaker, and Captain Stockton!"

Until the last roar of the afternoon. Before its echoes have ceased, new sounds are heard: shrieks of the torn and dying, shouts for help.

And as if by magic the man-of-war has become a funerary barge carrying home to the nation's capital the bodies of Secretary of State Upshur, Secretary of the Navy Gilmer, Captain Kennon, Colonel Gardiner, Mr. Maxey, and a servant of the president. President John Tyler, unharmed only by the sheer good luck of lingering below when the others went topside, rushed to help. But now he is in the wardroom below amidst the turmoil of grieving for the dead and caring for the wounded; he sits ashen and immobile, staring at the overturned glasses on his disheveled banquet.

An official Court of Inquiry soon find that on February 28, 1844, the two cabinet officers and four others were killed by a massive rupture of the breech of a new cannon mounted on the deck of the new fighting ship *Princeton*. Fifteen feet long, with a 12-inch bore, and weighing ten tons, "The Peacemaker" had already shown a large and festive party of leading politicians and two hundred of their ladies over and over the awful power of the armament of the Navy's newest warship. When still another exercise of the huge gun was requested, *Princeton*'s commander, Robert F. Stockton, had at first resisted. But the secretary of the Navy insisted, and the commander realized it was an order. Stockton had been standing right beside the big gun and was injured in the blast that killed the secretary, but managed nevertheless to play a creditable role in the care of the other wounded before he collapsed.[2]

"Horrible. Most horrible." wrote Philip Hone, the former mayor of New York, in his diary for Thursday, February 29, 1844: "An express arrived at two o'clock bringing an account of an awful disaster which occurred yesterday about four p.m. on board Capt. Stockton's steam-frigate *Princeton* – the vessel which was here a few weeks ago, fitted up with Ericsson's propellers, and carrying an enormous wrought-iron gun...This murderous projectile was called 'The Peacemaker'; and most deplorably has it earned its name, by making in an instant the peace of several of the most distinguished men of the country...It exploded at a time when there was a party on board of five hundred ladies and gentlemen, including the President and heads of departments...with their families, naval and military officers, senators and members of the House of Representatives, and all the distinguished persons resident and visiting at Washington..."[3] Such a disaster in such company called for an official investigation. A Naval Court was set up. Ericsson received a summons to Washington.

"How differently should I have regarded an *invitation* from Captain Stockton a week ago," Ericsson wrote back. "I might then have had it in my power to render good service and valuable counsel...I have to state most emphatically that since Captain Stockton is in possession of an accurate working plan of his exploded gun my presence at Washington can be of no use. ...

"With the sincerest wish that Captain Stockton may now have sufficiently recovered to bear with the fatigue of hearing you read this, I am, Yours truly, J. Ericsson."[4]

It was a decision that cost Ericsson dearly. In his absence, Stockton was able to make so much of Ericsson's having been responsible for the final steps in fabrication of the "Peacemaker," the boring and finishing of the weapon, that the court exonerated the naval officer, saying that he had relied properly on the advice of three experts, Ericsson among them – all civilians. The Navy's skirts were clean.

At this critical moment, President Tyler found it good to send his emissary, Robert F. Stockton, commanding the *U.S.S. Princeton*, to the Republic of Texas, bearing the documents of annexation into the United States. Doubtless, the commander was glad to get out of town. And to stay awhile. Stockton was soon sent out to take charge of protecting American interests in Mexican territory on the West Coast. He did this so flamboyantly that the American papers dubbed him "Conqueror of California." A city in California now bears his name. Success with the Delaware and Raritan Canal followed, and he was elected to the United States Senate.

But in the meantime a surprise was in store for Ericsson. Expert or not, when he at this late date presented his bill for two years of work and incident expenses, totaling over $15,000, the Navy referred it to Stockton, who responded that "Ericsson came to the United States without my invitation or approbation...much to my surprise and annoyance. Having thus thrust himself upon me, and believing him at that time to be a mechanic of some skill, *I did not employ him, but I permitted him, as a particular act of favor and kindness* , to superintend the construction of the machinery of the *Princeton* ...Ericsson himself considered, at the time he thus volunteered his services, that the opportunity afforded him to exhibit to the world the importance of his various patents, would be a satisfactory remuneration for all his services..."[5]

The Navy returned Ericsson's bill unpaid. He was going to spend the rest of his life trying, with the help of his lawyer John O. Sargent, to get it paid, first in the courts and then in unsuccessful applications to Congress.

"It is unfortunate," Ericsson wrote to his lawyer, "that ... immediately on the success of the *Princeton* I did not pack up my trap[ping]s, make a present of my inventions to the United States, and recross the Atlantic with a grateful heart to find my retreat left open, an advantage which I do not now enjoy."[6]

Stockton's insulting lie was a bitter lesson for Ericsson. It hardened him in a new resolve: never again would he risk being characterized as "an ingenious mechanic." The lust for tinkering, the lure of the machine shop, the itch to be hands-on (*never mind* theory) he now repressed in himself. Henceforth, whatever it might cost him, he would accept only the role of Guiding Intelligence, wielding the pencil rather than the hammer.

He is alone, isolated, adrift in the rough waters of the "*Princeton* " disgrace he has not merited. It is like being on one of those rafts of logs he has seen as a boy, floating down the Swedish rivers to the sawmill, whirling in the currents. When the rafts massed and jammed, intrepid men leaped from log to log, heaving and prying. If he only knew where to throw his weight!

It is more comforting to dream back even earlier, when, in a circle of safety borne by his father's hand, he followed Olof down into the mine. The lantern Olof lighted, so pale at the head of the mineshaft, makes a circle of light that encloses just the two of them as they descend into darkness.

It is of the mine itself John has made one of his first childish models, fashioning little miners out of twigs, each with a hammer, and placing a crude but well-proportioned hoisting wheel at the top of the little pit that represents the mine shaft they are now entering.

They descend level below level, each rough passage branching severally wherever the lode of iron has led. It is a man-made maze that nevertheless is casually navigable by Olof, a mining company manager who is the son of a mine owner who was the son of a miner. Nothing can be more natural than to walk inside the earth. The boy's eyes, wide in the darkness, see that submerged passageways can be a safe and natural place to do a man's work.

Now, adrift on memory, isolated on the raft of his exile and disgrace, John Ericsson experiences a sudden inspiration. In a flash he visualizes a novel solution to the central problem of naval warfare.

Against the whole history of fighting ships, and seemingly in the face of its waterborne logic, he will design a ship whose crew do the work of war almost entirely below the surface, as immune to shot and shell as miners are to hailstones. They will tend the engines and hoist the supplies of powder and shot to the cannon in the same submerged passageways where they find their lodging and sustenance at other times, enclosed in a kind of mine under the sea.

Their fighting ship protrudes above the surface hardly more than a raft. Only the eye and the fist of this fighter – the wheelhouse for lookout, command and steering and the cannon turret wheeling to attack in any direction – need project above the water and take the direct blows of the enemy.

John Ericsson begins to build a scale model...

NOTES

1. Report of Captain Robert Stockton to Navy Department, Feb. 5, 1844, in Church, William C., 1906, i, 129.
2. Sioussat, St. George L., 1937. See also Miles, A.H., 1926, 1-11.
3. Hone, Philip, Feb. 29, 1844 in Diary 1828-1851, 1970.
4. Ericsson, John to William. H. Thompson, Mar. 1, 1844, in Church, 1906, i, 141.
5. Stockton to Navy Department, May 20, 1844, in Church, 1906, i, 143-5.
6. Ericsson, John to John O. Sargent, July 20, 1846

CHAPTER 5

"He had very experienced superintendents," Samuel W. Taylor said, "who daily reported upon the work and from these reports [Ericsson] could tell the exact condition of things in the ship yard and machine shop, and thus be guided [as to] what work, in the nature of drawings, he should next perform to hurry up the completion of the work."

In a civil suit brought in a New York court in 1890,[1] Samuel W. Taylor was asked by the Court to describe the working methods of the late, renowned inventor, based on his observations from the time in 1862 he was first hired as Ericsson's clerk, through his service to Ericsson as private secretary from 1864 through 1889.

Question: "How was it possible for Capt. Ericsson to take entire charge of the construction of such extensive and complicated pieces of work without himself personally seeing the work in the course of construction. How could he tell for example whether certain parts of the machinery would in fact operate in accordance with his expectations if he did not himself see such machinery?"

*A*nswer: "It is impossible for me to tell. He used to explain it that being a thoroughly practical engineer an expert and accurate draughtsman possessing very great executive ability knowing always exactly what he wanted, that through intelligent and expert superintendents he always knew what was going on even to the minutest detail of the work that was being built for him and he considered a personal supervision a waste of the time that should be devoted to his drawing table in connection with his work in hand. He made all his working drawings himself and thus from time to time made himself thoroughly acquainted with the conditions of the work outside."

Q. "...Can you mention some important work or experiment carried on by him outside of his house which he did not himself personally see and inspect during its continuance."

A. "The building and completion of a fleet of monitors, not one of which he ever saw to my knowledge until after it had been engaged in the attack on Fort Sumpter [*sic*]. He did not visit the *Dictator* and *Puritan*, the two largest monitors built, excepting on the days of their being launched ... A fleet of Spanish gun boats thirty in number with their machinery and armament built from his design were not visited by him, and numerous other instances could be given. ...

"I was also sent to look at work he was engaged upon and report to him what I saw. He was then building the monitor fleet for the United States Government." Taylor took a wider purchase on the question. "...I was to observe everything as though I looked at things with his eyes, as I knew he never went out anywhere. ...

"All letters written by Capt. Ericsson himself were copied by me and thus I became intimately acquainted with what was transpiring from day to day. ...

"I was his principal means of communicating to him what was going on that was personally interesting to him in the world outside his house."

The Court asked Taylor what business, if any, he had been engaged in prior to 1862.

"I left school at the age of sixteen and a half and entered the employ of a clerk of a Court of Record in England," he related. In "a couple of years" he had mastered a fine, flowing handwriting. This was in a day when the typewriter was just being invented, and a clear, readable handwriting was still a marketable commodity. His "fair hand" enabled him, when he emigrated to America in 1858, to find employment as a copying clerk with John O. Sargent, who happened to be John Ericsson's lawyer. Contracts, applications for patent, and correspondence of all kinds had to be transcribed. "In April or May 1859" the young Englishman was dispatched to carry a message to the inventor.

Taylor's work was so "fair" that Ericsson, after that first meeting, repeatedly sought the help of his lawyer's young clerk. He must have liked the 25-year-old Anglo- Saxon, and found the King's English that came off Samuel Taylor's tongue enviable or, possibly, after his 13 years in England, sentimental.

Whether it was for these reasons or because he saw something of himself in the enterprising young immigrant, in 1862 Ericsson hired Taylor away to be his own clerk. Taylor's value to the inventor can be seen even today, comparing any of the hundreds of letters Taylor transcribed with elegant readability in both English and Swedish languages (it was his copy that was usually mailed) with the P.S. the inventor sometimes added in his own hasty, elliptical style.

In the 1880s, after typewriters came into wide use, the inventor had Samuel Taylor copy even incoming typewritten letters into his own flowing hand before Ericsson would deign to read them. If this service seems onerous, consider that Ericsson, before finding Taylor, had told a friend he was looking for someone "quick and dependable, uneducated and completely unacquainted with all those things that are most vital to me – a machine that works faithfully in accordance with the instructions, lacking the ability to pass judgment about even one of the subjects that occupy me."[2] Taylor filled the bill: in 1864, after two years as a clerk, Taylor was promoted to private secretary.

"My relations with Captain Ericsson were of a closer and more confidential character than what I should suppose would ordinarily exist between an employer and an employee," Taylor testified in court. "Capt. Ericsson had withdrawn from personal intercourse with nearly everyone. I took charge of all his domestic affairs and other matters personal to himself of a confidential nature.

"I received fully ninety per cent of the persons who called on him, whatever might be their object, and had authority from him to dismiss them without making communication with Capt. Ericsson of the visitor's desires to meet him personally or otherwise."

One of those who early gained admittance was Axel Adlersparre, a Swedish nobleman who once, as a young man, had spent six years working as an ordinary seaman on American merchant ships. Now a commodore in the Swedish navy and the assistant naval minister, Adlersparre had witnessed the *Monitor*'s battle at Hampton Roads and was en route home through New York. He wrote the hero of the hour asking for an interview. That Ericsson could be a gracious host to Swedish visitors is evident from Adlersparre's letter of thanks after their meeting:

"Before leaving America, I must yield to my heart's desire and in a few words present you, Captain, with my humble expression of gratitude for all the kindness and patience you accorded me. My meeting with you has been the choicest and most agreeable experience that has befallen me in many a year – and all the more so, that I am convinced that the welfare of our homeland will be advanced thereby to no small extent. Like every patriotic Swede I invoke heaven's blessings upon you, Captain, and I feel assured that one who so nobly sacrifices himself for the general good as you do shall undoubtedly reap a well-earned reward."[3]

Adlersparre's tone of fervent admiration would continue through most of the ensuing 15-year correspondence between them, but his reference to Ericsson's Swedish patriotism was no mere flattery. Though he had become an American citizen in 1848, Ericsson made no secret of another fealty; in a letter to William Seward, American secretary of state, he said "I love Sweden and would willingly sacrifice my life for her honor."[4]

He soon validated this pledge of allegiance by enabling Swedish authorities to copy his working drawings for the *Monitor*[5] and, once they had constructed their own ironclad, donating a 15-inch cannon for her armament. Adlersparre acknowledged the latter gift in a tone even more fervent: "If there is in heaven a special dwelling place for patriots, your place will certainly be in the state apartments."[6]

Ericsson had acquired his first and best Swedish "superintendent," whom he would "employ" for years to come.

Nor was Ericsson's hospitality to Swedish travelers only a late product of his ironclad-given fame and wealth. In May, 1856, a young Swedish baron had come calling. Bearing a letter of introduction from John's brother Nils, Baron Adelswärd happened to contact the inventor precisely on the anniversary of Ericsson's departure from Sweden thirty years before.

"He received me in a friendly spirit," the young man wrote his mother, "and was kind enough to promise he would send me a note when his caloric machine was running."

The "caloric" hot-air engine, conceived before Ericsson ever left Sweden, he advanced as a safer and thriftier alternative to the steam engine. His design for it evolved. Just a year before Adelswärd's visit, in 1855, Ericsson had patented an improved version of it. He was even designing a ship to be propelled by a scaled-up caloric engine. But it was a smaller "caloric" used for pumping water and other laborious household tasks that succeeded, much later, in finding a profitable market.

"[Subsequently] I made a visit in the company of Captain Ericsson," Baron Adelswärd continued, "to a workshop where he had one of his caloric machines. Unfortunately it was still not running and would not be ready for operation until the day of my departure. Nevertheless he gave me the most thorough description, and judging by this his main problem with it seems to have been solved.

"After we had looked at the machine he invited me to join him in a meal at the best restaurant in New York. We raised a glass of champagne to grand old Sweden, to his early return to Sweden, and to a fortunate homeward journey for me, and so on. After that I walked home with him, where he gave me several letters to his brother with drawings and documents that authorize his brother, the colonel, to take out patents in Sweden for his new modifications to the caloric machine."[7]

However, Ericsson's hospitality had its limits. Too many Swedes wrote to him, even before his success with the *U.S.S. Monitor*, asking him to advise them about, or even to sponsor the immigration of their sons and brothers. "On no account send any youth here," he wrote to one such supplicant. "A Swedish engineer has nothing to learn here. Confining work, trade fraud and superficial show are all this country has to offer."[8]

He assured a high Swedish official that "in the 30 years I have lived in this country, I have not *in a single case* advised a countryman to come here. On the contrary, I have paid out substantial sums to help Swedes return to the home country."[9]

And yet he would welcome a visit from any Swede who came well-recommended or whose attention might prove useful to him. Among these was a journalist, Mauritz Rubenson, sent to America in 1868 by the *Gothenburg Trade and Shipping Journal* to write travel articles. He described his visit to Ericsson's home on Beach Street:

"Soon I stood before No. 36. I hesitated a moment, hardly able to believe in my own good luck – I was about to meet the world-renowned inventor face to face! Before I touched the doorbell, I opened still again the briefcase I was carrying in which I had conveyed the photographs from celebrations at Långbanshyttan in Värmland. Oh, how glad I felt at seeing in these photos how Swedes took pleasure in celebrating their memories of this man, whom they had learned to love and admire for his genius, character and devotion to their homeland. My hand grasped the doorbell, and the metallic sound had not died away before the door opened and a middle-aged man invited me in English to kindly step inside.

"When I had told him my errand, and had been shown into an entrance hall, this man left me, as he said, to inform Captain E. of my visit.

"Now, while I am waiting, I would like to tell you a little about the place where I found myself. It is on the ground floor, and connected with another, larger room. A round table stands in the middle of the floor holding a book in which all who come to visit Captain E. write their names.

"On each side of the stove are two more tables. On these are exhibited under glass bells a number of models of various mechanical inventions. On a pedestal in one corner stands a bust of one of Captain E.'s American friends. On the wall is seen a certificate of honor from the City of New York awarded to the excellent creator of the *Monitor*.

"After a wait of a few minutes, someone is heard quickly descending the stairs and in a moment I was meeting one of the century's most celebrated persons.

"After greeting him, I handed him, with only a few words, the photographs from Långbanshyttan. This was one of the most interesting moments of my entire trip. To see how this warmhearted friend of our homeland was overcome with emotion, how for a long minute he stood as if nailed to the floor, gazing at these memories of his childhood, the cottage where he had spent his boyhood – this, words cannot convey.

"At last he said: 'Yes, I recognize my old home,' and in the same moment a few tears slipped from his eyes that had certainly come from the wellsprings of his heart." In his gratitude, the inventor lent the visiting reporter the services of Samuel Taylor to guide him around New York.[10]

On a summer day in 1876, another Swedish visitor stood at the door of No. 36 Beach Street. He may well have turned about, after ringing the doorbell, to look across the street at a noisy railroad freight yard that had displaced the lovely park that graced the neighborhood when Ericsson moved in years ago. Railroads and their equipment were this visitor's business.

Fifty-two years old, distinguished in appearance and with the highest of recommendations, he had told the famous inventor's nephew and namesake, Baron John Ericson, a member of the Swedish parliament, of his plan to travel from Philadelphia to New York especially to meet the Swedish-American hero.But Ericsson, when told of the plan, had written:

"A visit from Hjalmar will be unpleasant in many respects. If he is wise, he will refrain from calling on me without having first received an invitation."[11]

NOTES

1. Suit of M.C. Heath against Estate of Captain John Ericsson, New York, Nov. 28, 1890.
2. Ericsson, John to Axel Adlersparre, Mar. 20, 1868, in Margaretha J. Runvik, 1996, 121-2.
3. Goldkuhl, Carola, 1961, 186.
4. Church, William C., 1906, ii, 122. In an 1869 letter to the Swedish foreign minister Carl Wachtmeister, Ericsson said: "I am certainly an American citizen, but nevertheless I consider it my greatest honor to be a Swedish subject. The modern cosmopolitan spirit has no attractions for me and should events require it, my life and all I own are at the service of His Majesty the King and my homeland," in Goldkuhl, 1961, 224.
5. The Danes asked the U.S. Navy Department through diplomatic channels whether they might do the same, and were turned down.
6. Church, 1906, ii, 120.
7. Private communication from Johan T. Adelswärd, November 22, 2002, providing a facsimile of his "excerpt copy in Swedish...the original letters [from his ancestor] are in French."
8. Ericsson to M.F. Gussander, Feb., 1866, in Runvik, 1996, 130.
9. Ericsson to Wachtmeister as cited Note 4 above.
10. Rubenson, Mauritz, 1868, 97-9, 107-8.
11. Ericsson to Baron John Ericson, 1876, in Runvik, 1996, 144.

CHAPTER 6

Hjalmar Elworth might well have glanced up and down Beach Street with an expression of surprise. The Hudson River Railroad depot across the street with its clatter and creak of heavily laden wagons bringing freight, its trains with their hissing steam and slamming clangor, and down the block the squeals and shouts of children spilling out of workers' tenements made this seem an unlikely neighborhood for the home and drafting office of a world-famous inventor and national hero.

But the visitor's face may also have betrayed a special excitement. Was it the anticipation anyone might feel when about to meet a celebrated person? Elworth was used to meeting celebrities back in Stockholm, the capital of Sweden. A member of the Governing Board of the new Swedish Railways and a deputy to its Director,[1] he would have been among the official party, for example, when King Carl XV cut the ribbon to dedicate still another newly opened railway station. He might well have shared in the compliments of the prime minister for the station's architecture, since he was the chief inspector of facilities and equipment.

More recently, in Philadelphia where America's International Centennial Exhibition was in progress, Hjalmar Elworth was one of 15 prominent specialists sent by Sweden to observe and report on American progress in railroad engineering, metallurgy, mechanical engineering, and other technical fields as well as education and the fine arts.

Prince Oscar of Sweden also attended the world's fair. Elworth was in the party when the young prince traveled to nearby Delaware to visit what little now remained of New Sweden, the first Swedish settlement in America (1638-1655). In this party Elworth was among friends.[2]

Sweden had a long tradition of enabling technically qualified persons to travel abroad to seek out industrial or scientific knowledge for the homeland's use. In 1694 Christopher Polhem, the founding giant of Swedish engineering, received support from King Karl XI for travels to Germany, Holland, England, Belgium, France, Switzerland and Denmark, and on his return enriched the industry of his native country out of a memory well stored with observed machines and processes.[3] Linnaeus, the Swedish botanist who invented the system of scientific classification that is still in use today, sent 10 of his most promising assistants and students abroad. They traveled to Japan, the East Indies, China, Arabia, South and North America, and even along with Captain Cook on the voyage that circled the earth. Their observations and reports helped make Sweden an 18th century scientific superpower.[4]

The tradition continued into the 19th century. In the second half of the 1800s Sweden sent to the United States alone nearly 300 accomplished practitioners of every industrial skill of the time. They received grants from their government to visit, experience directly, carefully observe and report home foreign solutions to technical problems. In America, iron and steel production, power generation, newspaper printing machinery and building construction were among the objects of their study.[5]

Elworth came to America in 1876 on such a grant. He brought two special wishes. One was to find a better design for a railroad snow plow to use on the new Swedish railways. He was helping to create the railroad network that would eventually become the circulatory system of a rapidly industrializing 1,000-mile-long country with long, snowy winters. He was in charge of one of the railroad's four departments, responsible for equipment both fixed and moving, for facilities from workshops to passenger stations, and for the track network. Some have said that his contributions to the establishment of the Swedish Railways rank second only to Nils Ericson's.

Elworth's second special wish would have been understandable in any Swede of the time. He wanted to meet John Ericsson, the Swedish American, whose *U.S.S. Monitor* warship had saved the Union blockade of Confederate ports and made him famous in many countries. But he had another reason as well. Hjalmar Elworth was John Ericsson's only son, though born out of wedlock, and at 52 years of age he had never met his father.

Before leaving Sweden Hjalmar had confided this wish to his cousin Baron John Ericson, who passed it along to the great man. It is easy to imagine Hjalmar Elworth's feelings when he learned of the reply his cousin had received from America: *"If [Hjalmar] is wise he will refrain from calling on me without having first received an invitation."*[6]

Nevertheless, John Ericsson's son was standing here at the door of No. 36 Beach Street in New York City, and the door opened.

Who answered his knock? Louis, Ericsson's Italian manservant, might have opened the door, or perhaps Ann Cassidy, his Irish housekeeper. Amelia, Ericsson's English wife, was not here; she had long since returned to England for good. Elworth was received with courtesy, no doubt; Ericsson's standing instructions were that even panhandlers were to be received and, if deserving, helped. But apparently his son was received without ceremony.

Like any celebrity, Ericsson had walk-in visitors, the idly curious. These, Samuel Taylor dealt with expeditiously. But Ericsson's "superintendents" of ongoing projects must also have come in every day to report. It is said that Hjalmar Elworth was simply directed to the end of the queue. One supposes that his calling card was carried up to the busy inventor. Ericsson may not have hastened to lay aside his pencil for a visit he expected to be "unpleasant ... in many respects."

How understandable if Hjalmar Elworth felt that, after 52 years, he had already waited his turn to see John Ericsson. How incredible if he did not deeply resent being queued with subordinates expected to make a report. It was John Ericsson himself who had some explaining to do...

Elworth may have had ample time to glare at the models under their cupolas of glass, and at the honorary certificate on the wall. Time to muse again over his relationship with his father.

There was a wide cold sea between parent, in America, and son, in Sweden. Since 1842, when he had relayed his greeting-cum-apology to Hjalmar, then 18, through his own mother,[7] Brita Sofia, John Ericsson had only communicated with his son through his brother Nils.

Yet it was an arrangement that benefited Hjalmar, whatever it cost him. Nils, near at hand, was not only his uncle but his mentor and friend. Nils and his wife Wilhelmina had three sons of their own and a daughter. From early on, Hjalmar was often in their home. When Hjalmar married, they were often invited to his.

Hjalmar's bent for engineering was evident while Nils' other sons seemed to have trouble choosing careers. After Hjalmar had completed a good technical education, Nils hired him to work on a series of his own projects, first in canal-building and then in railroad construction. He coached and encouraged Hjalmar, and his brother's son became his best understudy. When Nils retired (with a peerage and a handsome pension) he designated Hjalmar as one of his several successors in the direction of the new railroad.

Nils wrote to Hjalmar in 1865 that his father, in America, "has often spoken of your debt to me for the sacrifices I have made to give you an education. I can now gladden you with the news that John has not only liquidated those outlays, but also the five expenses and costs I have borne for him during all these years we have been apart. So he now has no further debt to me, and had your debt not also been discharged, it would never have been presented to you. Through your conduct, your intelligence and your merits, not to mention your devotion to me and mine, you have richly repaid those small expenses I had for your youth."[8]

Nils also suggested to John Ericsson that Hjalmar and his wife Sophie really ought to be included in his will; John responded positively from America. But when Nils wrote Hjalmar of these prospects, the young man wrote back:

"Concerning the question of a bequest to me once offered by my father, I would really prefer to know nothing of the matter. My father does not seem to hold any kind of warmer feelings for me, since to this day he has not taken the smallest step toward getting us together... However I must recognize with the warmest gratitude my Uncle's goodness and interest for me in this matter. I think that on several previous occasions I had only my Uncle's efforts to thank for what I obtained from my father. He seems to have always been entirely indifferent to me personally, and therefore I find it hard to believe that he will do anything for me of any importance."[9]

When Nils died suddenly in 1870, of infection following an operation, Hjalmar's connection to his biological father seemed to have been severed as well. Yet it was John Ericsson who finally got in touch. In 1872 Hjalmar received on his birthday a printed copy of a technical paper his father had written, though without any personal message inscribed. But it had been mailed from New York, and Hjalmar took it for a sign that finally, after almost five decades of his life, direct contact with his father was now permissible.

"Long ago I wanted to transmit my gratitude to you," Hjalmar wrote back, "and asked my Uncle Nils, while he lived, if I should not write, but he thought it unsuitable since you had not written first to me."

John Ericsson's answer to these thanks has not survived. But whatever the father wrote, he could not have prepared his son for this rebuff: *"...refrain from calling on me without having first received an invitation."* Nevertheless, here he was at John Ericsson's door, invited or not. Perhaps, with a whole new continent before him, Hjalmar Elworth was emboldened to shrug aside the Old World constraints.

Sooner or later John Ericsson did descend from his work to meet his only son face-to-face. By that time Hjalmar Elworth had been escorted into a private room furnished with a few hard chairs and a table for Ericsson's supervisors to spread out their drawings and reports.

Hjalmar gets to his feet, for he sees through the doorway, descending the stairs, a man who resembles the photographs he has seen of his father. Clenched as Hjalmar is, he is touched when he sees a face veiled in the old, dear familiarities, aspects of other faces that spoke to him in his own earlier life, all of them now in the grave...Nils Ericson... Brita Sofia Ericsson...Anna Carolina Odhner... He is almost disarmed. But these are veils that part, as the old man advances toward him, to reveal – an absolutely unexpected expression. It reminds Hjalmar that, after all, his name is Elworth.

What his father's face expresses is so complex that it will nourish Hjalmar's ruminations for years to come. He sees recognition, something he has come a long way for, yes. But also an intense, troubled scrutiny. And just possibly, if his anger does not warp his vision, the lightest flush of shame, a lurking glint of...can it be fear? Fear on John Ericsson's face?

He feels the old man's hand graze his, and by reflex he shakes it. And this mechanical gesture is the lever that engages an equally mechanical discipline of courtesy. He has never allowed himself an outburst and he will not now, full though he is of 52 years' warring impulses, for now he is facing his own father. And John Ericsson? His first sight of Hjalmar from the stairway was of a figure, a shape which Ericsson, as he descended the stairs, was fitting and re-fitting like a puzzle piece into a pattern he identifies with his brother Nils. Yes, that set of the jaw, that particular angle of the shoulders, yes, just as he thought, Nils' imprimatur is on his son.

And, just as he has feared, this sight of Nils, even Nils reflected in Hjalmar his own son, opens anew his bitter, complicated grief: *Nils is dead. Never to be reconciled now. Was I wrong not to return?* He has silenced this inner voice before, he knows the way. He must ready himself for other questions. He puts out his hand—

When, suddenly, with a pang that has been waiting for him 52 years, John Ericsson sees *her* face, *Carolina Lilliesköld's* face.

"How much you look like your mother!" John Ericsson exclaims.

Would Samuel Taylor, the inventor's factotum, have discreetly withdrawn from an interview so likely to become emotional? We can hope so, though Ericsson's rebuff to Hjalmar's travel plans makes it seem that privacy to share emotions with his son was the last thing he wanted. Though he had been moved to tears by photographs of his home in Långbanshyttan brought him by a stranger, this was a different kind of picture. He may have bidden his secretary to remain, so the meeting would remain formal and superficial.

It may be to Taylor we owe the only extant record of their first conversation: *How much you look like your mother!*[10] In English!

The rest is a mystery. Yet, we have a very good idea what was on Hjalmar Elworth's mind to say. We have all of his very first letter to his father, both in draft and in final form. It was written after he received in 1872, on his 48th birthday, the printed paper in which John Ericsson retorted to another engineer's published criticisms of his solar experiments. Hjalmar seized this thin, dry finger of recognition extended to him out of John Ericsson's knotty fist of rhetorical retribution, this slim sheaf of printed anger. Admiring a father known to all the world but denied, in any real terms, to himself, Hjalmar took this cold and folded smudge for an invitation at last *to be* – to be the only son of a real, if distant father – "though of course a few handwritten lines would have pleased me a lot more..." To his father's strange message he eagerly responded:

"When for the first time, now in my 48th year, I speak to my father, I do so with a heart moved and grateful for all that my father has done for me, enabling me to attain without indebtedness the respected position in society that is now mine...

"I want to tell you that I am on the Governing Board of the National Railway Operating System as Chief Inspector for Equipment and Facilities..." His salary and its deductions, the help his wife's thrifty management gave in making ends meet, his contentment with the rank he had achieved, since the very highest position in the enterprise would have entailed representation he would not have been able to afford even on the higher salary – these homely details filled out his presentation of himself.

Then he went on into the technical realm, as if to demonstrate that he was qualified to appreciate, from inside the engineering sphere, his father's great accomplishments. Had his father any advice for him? He was seeking a successful American design for the snow plow so badly needed by his own Swedish railway to handle drifts deeper than 5 or 6 feet.

And just how did his father's solar power machine work, how could it store the sun's heat, and what did it cost to produce?[11]

Apparently John Ericsson did reply to this first letter from his son, though his letter has not survived. Conceivably, Ericsson may have lauded his son's accomplishments, complimented his choice of a thrifty, supportive wife, recommended a better snow plow and explained the mechanics and economics of his solar machine. We have no way of knowing.

Hjalmar's little list of thanks and circumstances and interests is all that a caring parent would have needed on which to build an hour's warm exchanges. Yet this first meeting between them in New York was said to have been memorable mostly for its brevity.

Can it be that Hjalmar's official role in the Centennial Exhibition was a bitter pill for Ericsson? He knew by now that hardly any of his work, other than a wooden model of the *Monitor* turret that he took as an affront, would be displayed among what President U.S. Grant would celebrate, on opening day, as America's "attainments in the industrial... arts...and...science."

Yet Hjalmar had been chosen by the Swedish authorities to attend as an honored guest. Elworth explained to his father that, since he was in charge of equipment and facilities for Sweden's young and growing railway system, he and his superiors considered this exhibition an opportunity to observe American railroad innovations; four years after he had first asked his father's advice, he was still looking for the ideal snow plow.

In fact, he was about to make a transcontinental study tour of American and Canadian railroads. This explanation must have stirred John Ericsson's memory. As a 26-year-old inventor in England, when railroads, too, were young, he had gambled everything on the prize competition for a steam locomotive design, and lost only by a hair. Evocation of his own railroading days may have made the meeting more interesting than he expected. But "many" aspects of Hjalmar's visit, he had written, "would be unpleasant."

Maybe he feared being called to account by this mature and distinguished son of his? What father has never been given pause by the thought of his son, his natural survivor and inheritor, some day being his judge? It is said that, over 50 years before, John had asked for the hand of Carolina, who would become Hjalmar's mother, and after he had been rejected by her parents in the most humiliating way, Ericsson left town.

At best, he had left behind unknowingly a son of whose existence he never heard until, more than two years later, he was an émigré in England vainly struggling to make a living. At worst, he left Hjalmar's mother in Stockholm, knowing she had been banished from her home because pregnant with his child, left her to fend for herself in a strange city while he went off to seek his fortune in England. Whichever was the true case, when he learned that Brita Sofia, his mother, had taken in his child to raise as her own, he contributed to the boy's maintenance whenever he could, and at last, in his prosperity, reimbursed it all. Yet there was plenty left to answer for:

Why, if he had wanted Carolina for his wife before her parents rejected him, did he not take her for his wife after they had cast her out, and so given Hjalmar the chance of a home? Why, if Hjalmar had to be reared by proxy, did Ericsson never visit his only son, and only communicate directly with him after 48 years?

Still another fear may have darkened John Ericsson's prospect of a visit from Hjalmar. If his son should demand such an accounting, Ericsson may have dreaded that he would be unable to answer easily and surely in his native tongue. Hjalmar, as far as we know, had only written him in Swedish.

"I am so entirely Swedish," Ericsson had once written, "that I cannot bear the thought that I am believed to have forgotten, or set aside in preference for some other, our beautiful mother tongue, 'the language of glory and heroes.'"[12]

Yet he also wrote to a Swedish admirer: "Overwhelmed with work, I have not had time to write the description you ask for in my native tongue. I can think in English four times faster than I can write in Swedish, and write four times faster than I can think."[13]

Or the explanation why he dreaded a visit from Hjalmar may be even simpler. John Ericsson may have fallen into the same deep green trap that always lies in wait for a self-made man face-to-face with his own son: "He *must* be *spoiled*. After all, he's had *everything I never had*."

NOTES

1. Private communication from Birgitta Hansson, Public Affairs, SJ AB [Swedish Railways, Inc.] April 2, 2003.
2. Dardel, Fritz von, 1916, 212-213.
3. Westerlund, Kerstin, 2000, 9-10.
4. Schildt, Göran, 1960, 7-10.
5. Hagerman, Maja, 1981, 7.
6. Ericsson, John to Baron John Ericson, April 1876, in Runvik, Margaretha, 1996, 144, 156.
7. "Please give Hjalmar my warm greetings. The future will show him that I have not forgotten the duties of a father. The great scope of my projects has constantly impoverished me, not, as Mother thinks, extravagance—"[the remainder of this line as well as the signature have been clipped off]. Ericsson, John, to Brita Sofia Ericsson, Nov. 30, 1842.
8. Ericson, Nils to Elworth, 1865, in Goldkuhl, Carola, 1957, 116.
9. Elworth, Hjalmar to Nils Ericson, ca. 1869, in Goldkuhl, 1961, 231-2.
10. We know that Ericsson confided the identity of his visitor to his secretary because Taylor confirmed it in a letter to Sophie Elworth dated March 29, 1889. "... Captain Ericsson, in assigning me the duty of escorting Mr. Elworth for certain occasions, said: 'It is important for your guidance to know that I am his father.' I have not endeavored to learn more than this..."
11. Church, William C., 1906, ii, 214.
12. Church, 1906, i, 7, quoting in English a letter Ericsson "wrote in the midst of his triumphs," i.e. around 1862, and evidently in Swedish, since it quotes a famous Swedish poet, Esaias Tegnér.
13. Church, 1906, i, 32, quoting in English a letter to a Swedish correspondent the biographer does not name, about 1876. Among Ericsson's correspondence are notes to various Swedish translators resident in New York.

II

In Sweden

CHAPTER 7

They had little enough left. Now it was gone. For John Ericsson, 7, and his brother Nils, 8 years old, and even for their older sister Anna Carolina, it must have been terrifying.

Their beds stood outdoors. The chairs and stools that belonged around their table when John and his brother and sister and mother and father sat down together were now straggling across the grass beyond the table. On the table were piled other belongings, each signaling an ownership, Mother's shawl, Nils' well-worn extra boots... Within the cabin, door agape, nothing was left but their dust. Out front of the cabin stood all the people John knew and some he had never seen. He thought he saw Jons Orsa, his playmate, hanging back in the throng, as if unwilling to greet him.[1] Their faces and low voices expressed feelings John could not identify. He saw the ashamed glances they gave Olof and Brita, his mother and father. He saw the looks, curious and even covetous, they cast on his family's exposed and somehow almost naked belongings.

Why were these people standing there whispering while the stranger who stood behind the furniture waited for their silent attention? What was it he had come to do with his paper and pencil and his little hammer?

Then the stranger cleared his throat loudly and began. He would point to Father's chair or Nils' stool or Mother Brita's pitcher and say something, and this person or that would call out a number. He would repeat every number in a curious singsong until suddenly he struck the table with his hammer, a loud and final crack! Then someone would step up to lay a few coins on the table and carry the thing away while the stranger scribbled on his paper.[2]

Bewildered, John looked to his parents for explanation and reassurance, but their faces were grim and taut as they, too, coped with an advancing, embracing emptiness. This was harder than they expected. It was not just shreds of ownership they were letting go, it was shreds of an identity. Souvenirs, paltry enough, of the many possessions they had started out with so buoyantly 10 years before. Anna Carolina started to cry.

A decade before, Olof, John Ericsson's father, had come over from a neighboring town to take a job as bookkeeper in an iron mining company in this village of Långbanshyttan. He was strongly attracted to the pretty, unusually well-educated daughter of his boss, the mining company manager, and she returned his interest. They were married. Both were 21 years old.[3]

At once, Olof was given the management of the mining company, and soon thereafter an imposing house with nine subsidiary buildings including a stable for 10 horses and a barn with 16 cows. The 21-year-old newlyweds had shares in the ownership of two local iron mines, a smelter, a forge, a sawmill, some woods and a fair amount of land.

In recognition of his new status, Olof was named to an arbitration board for mining disputes. Solemnly, he took an oath, gavel in hand, to be fair in the judgments he rendered. Now a man of substance, he felt he could give away to his brother the miner's work permit he had put aside when he started bookkeeping. But with his pretty bride and his new dignity he also gained the first of many debts. He had to buy out the shares of Brita's two brothers.

Strangely enough, within four years Olof had voluntarily given up his position as manager and lost its substantial salary. In five years, he had contracted so much debt that an auction of their still extensive property threatened, but Olof went to moneylenders and borrowed to stave this off. But he had borrowed on ruinous terms. By the sixth year of their marriage, Olof had to abandon a costly attempt to restore an abandoned silver mine nearby to production. In their eighth year together he and Brita lost the fine house along with all the other real estate and had to move their family, by now a daughter and two sons, into a two-room cabin on the very edge of their former holdings. Three cabin winters passed after they had vacated not only comforts but their standing in the community.[4]

These were desperate losses, but it should be noted that the Ericssons had unusual resources. Brita, an avid reader of Sir Walter Scott's novels, was no mean storyteller.

"Their surroundings made the fantasy creatures in her stories more vivid," a biographer has speculated. "There was the waterfall with wicked water spirits, and the dark forest where elves made their home. Beneath the earth mighty chambers extended where the king of the mountain dwelled. And at night, high into the starry heavens flared the flames of the smelters, where the ore from the mines was being transformed into white hot sparkling serpents."[5]

Olof had received a good education at the gymnasium (a kind of junior college) in his native town. He gained a lifelong admiration for Christopher Polhem (1661-1751), a Swedish inventor, engineer and philosopher who had earned the trust and support of Sweden's king Karl XII. When Olof later became the inspector of a mine, assigned to devise a way of transmitting the power from a water wheel across several hundred yards of land to a mine shaft, it was to an ingenious rod transmission system invented by Polhem that he turned. Polhem also had unusual ideas about education that may have influenced Olof in fostering his young sons. Certainly Olof passed along to John both the story of Polhem and his own knowledgeable interest in the science of the time.

"My delight," John Ericsson related 63 years later, "my delight, the first time I saw the column of water rise in a glass cylinder at the moment my father quenched the flame inside, can never be erased from my memory."[6]

For their instruction, Olof sometimes took his little boys along. As manager, he often had to go into the mine, or into the smelter or forge or sawmill. These visits, with their practical observations, especially stimulated John, who made his first little models of the machinery he saw. But when, for unknown reasons, Olof left the management of the iron mine and had to support his family as the foreman of a blasting crew, there would have been no more such educational excursions.

By 1809 Olof was unemployed.

The Ericssons' troubles had much larger dimensions. Almost immediately after Olof succeeded his father-in-law as mine manager, the iron in their mines began to play out. When they tried to go deeper to find new ore, water flooded up and repeatedly overcame their pumps. When they broke a drift in a new direction, they hit granite; no help there. Olof's successor as mining company manager had no more success than he.

Indeed, the whole mining industry was in trouble. The price of iron ore had dropped catastrophically because Sweden's trade with England, its best customer for iron, was under threat from Napoleon. When King Gustav IV Adolf of Sweden refused France's demand to cut off all trade with England, Russia, then Napoleon's ally, sent 24,000 soldiers into Sweden's Finnish province. Eventually the Russians entered northern Sweden itself and, occupying the island of Åland, threatened the capital Stockholm. "All of Finland disappeared from the kingdom of Sweden: a third of Sweden's land area, a fourth of its population. A million Swedish citizens became subjects of the Tsar..."[7]

How much of this could a 7-year-old boy have understood? None, but through his parents' steadily mounting anxiety and their inevitable quarrels and recriminations, the boy must already have sensed that his whole world was breaking apart – even before the auctioneer's hammer struck – *Gone, Gone, Gone!*

Olof could not even find risky work as a blasting crew chief any more, not in their village of Långbanshyttan. The war was making blasting powder unobtainable.

The country was at war not only with Russia but also with France and all of France's allies, with Prussia and the league of Rhenish states and Denmark and Norway.

One day, Olof and Brita heard that the Swedish army holding the border with Norway had been turned around by its commander and was now advancing on the Swedish capital. King Gustaf, who had lost Sweden's holdings in Finland and in Pomerania and placed the kingdom itself in jeopardy, had been deposed by his own officers. "Sweden had no king and no real government. It was at war and in a famine year, and in the capital lay a revolutionary army whose purposes and uses nobody could really foresee." [8]

At this moment of enormous turmoil and confusion, a letter came to Olof that promised work. And not just any sort of job, though he would have to become a blasting foreman again. He would be given a part in realizing a scheme that Christopher Polhem had proposed long ago, to build a ship canal across Sweden, connecting the Baltic Sea with the North Sea. Olof grew very excited.

Of course they would have to move to another province, a hundred miles off, where none of them had ever been. But by now Olof and Brita were of a mind to turn their backs on their decade of disaster. Even uncertainty among strangers seemed more welcoming than Långbanshyttan. Why not sell everything left – not much, at that – in order to make a last payment on their stubborn debts, and to get together a meager travel budget?

The auctioneer was contacted, and a date set. Some clothing was bundled up and put in an old wagon. The children were told that they were going to start over in a new place. Never having been anywhere but their birthplace, Långbanshyttan, they could hardly have understood. And how to convey to them that everything would be sold?

In their damaged pride Olof and Brita may have wanted to demonstrate to all those who had witnessed their ruin in Långbanshyttan that they were on their way to nothing less than a new life. They even left family papers behind.[9]

The day of departure arrived, and the cabin was emptied. What could John, 7, and Nils, 8, have made of this? *Swift dispossession and gaping homelessness. Losing every familiar object in an emotionally charged scene, these children glimpsed the abyss.*

John, at least, never forgot it. Many years later, in the days of his world fame, John Ericsson told his biographer that one of his earliest recollections was "the appearance of the sheriff selling the family furniture to satisfy the demands of importunate creditors."[10]

For John Ericsson, a small boy weeping before an empty cabin in Långbanshyttan, the hammer's fall was a judgment. A judgment against him and his family. For what crimes?

Unknowable to his tender understanding, but not the less terrible, when the sentence that was passed was banishment.

NOTES

1. Lindwall, Gustaf, 1937, 18. Many years later "Jons Orsa," Jonas Olsson received a sentimental greeting and a gift from John Ericsson.
2. Runvik, Margaretha, 1996, 9. See also Church, William C., 1906, i, 3,14; Hallerdt, Björn, 2003, 12, 16; Lindwall, 1937, 19.
3. Lindwall, 1937, 11-12.
4. Goldkuhl, Carola, 1961, 12-14. See also Hultman, H., 1949, 19, 49-51.
5. Lindwall, 1937, 18.
6. Lindwall, 1937, 28.
7. Lindquist, Herman, 1998, 187-8, 385-6.
8. Lindquist, 1998, 187-8.
9. Goldkuhl, 1961, 17.
10. Church, 1906, i, 3. See also Lindwall, 1937, 19.

CHAPTER 8

For the family jolting along in an old wagon, the close-spaced hills and frothing streams and dense woods of Värmland gave way to Västergötland, a rolling, spacious countryside surrounding bright lakes, where there seemed to be much more sky.

But 7-year-old John knew only the close embrace of Värmland's small valleys. Emerging beneath such strange lights may have given him an anxious premonition of embarking on strange seas.

All three children were watching their parents for cues to understanding the swift changes in their life. At first the faces of both their elders were strained, just as when, outside the cabin, Olof and Brita had seen their most accustomed possessions taken one by one. After all, it was their known world they were rolling away from. As the hours went by John saw Olof's face changing. It was as though it turned from a double-barred door to an opening portal, welcoming what came. For Olof, admiration's name was Christopher Polhem, and even jolting and swaying, they were headed toward the realization of Polhem's dream of a canal linking two seas, and he, Olof, would have a part in realizing it.

Yet little John saw no such transformation in Brita Sofia's face. She was leaving her lost patrimony. It was not so easy for her to relinquish for good the life-plan that on her wedding day had seemed assured. New uncertainties lay ahead, and her ten disastrous years with Olof had robbed her of something beyond price: her confidence in his judgment.

Why had Olof resigned from managing the mine company? Was he too young, did his partners make it plain they wanted a more seasoned leader in hard times? But had he shown mature judgment, pouring resources into a failed silver mine?

Certainly Brita Sofia's rapid descent from the manager's house to a cabin, from relative riches and security to poverty and vulnerability, began with marrying Olof. Is it reasonable to suppose she never gave vent to her feelings, was incapable of recrimination?

Some degree of disaffection between them may have sown the seeds of a schism that later arose between Nils, the elder brother, and John, the younger. Brita Sofia would henceforth bend her best efforts to make Nils incapable of what she may have considered Olof's follies. But John's devotion to Olof was unshakeable, and it would prove lifelong.

Brita Sofia knew their family had to leave the decade's losses behind, had to seize this opportunity. She knew, as Olof did, that near Långbanshyttan public soup kitchens were being set up to feed unemployed miners something boiled up out of cattle's blood and bones.

After days of swaying and jolting in the rude wagon, frowsy and aching they came at last to Forsvik. It was a scene of feverish activity. What had been a mere village was rapidly becoming something between a mill and an encampment. Barracks were being built for hundreds and hundreds of soldiers. They would dig the great trench for the new canal with ordinary picks and shovels, once the blasting crew had shattered the rock and the stone. In this way, Olof and his crew would be leading them.

A clinic was open, and offices. Doors swung open and people kept both going in and coming out at once. Forges and mechanical shops had been set up to make and repair the hard-used hand tools, and to forge mechanical parts for the lock gates. Storage sheds for lumber and dressed stone and other building materials were being hammered together, a din that seemed almost cheerful after the gloomy silence they had left behind in their home village.[1]

But where, among all these new structures, was the center of this swirl of activity? Olof had been told to present himself at headquarters. He flagged a passerby and asked the way.

The stranger listened with furrowed intensity, but when he replied it was with a question in some other language. It was Olof's turn to furrow his brow, but Brita volunteered "He must be speaking English." Her musings over Swedish translations of Scott's romances, with all their Anglo-Saxon place names, might have given her the clue.

Whatever language the stranger was speaking, he shrugged at Olof's confusion and hailed still another passerby. This man understood Olof's question, but when he replied, his accent was so foreign to little John's ears that it might as well have been English. In this miniature Babel of a camp where English and German and Dutch and the dialects of half Sweden's provinces were heard every day young John Ericsson's keen curiosity found a wholly new object.

The man's gesturing directions led Olof to a sizable building where, through large windows, men were seen leaning over drawing tables.

Olof Ericsson tied up the old horse and left his family in the wagon while he went looking for the man to whom he had been told to report. He was gone a long time, but the family was completely absorbed in the noisy, energetic spectacle all around them.

When he returned, he brought the news that accommodations in the headquarters building had been allotted to the Ericssons. The family found their new quarters, and moved in – the work of a few minutes. The father returned to the head office for further talk about the plans and schedules for blasting to initiate the building of a canal across Sweden linking the Baltic Sea with the North Sea.

When Olof returned, he brought another piece of news – this time, the offer of some help for the family's badly damaged economy. A canteen was being set up for the engineers, draftsmen and supervisors, and someone able to cook and willing to serve meals to busy professional men every day was needed to run it. Was Brita Sofia willing?

It could not have taken her long to decide.

She was soon at work while her small children once more enjoyed the sights and smells and tastes that came from a well-stocked busy kitchen.

Some of her clientele had come from other countries. Among the banter and shop talk in the dialects of Sweden could be heard quite a lot of English. The island nation where the technology of canal building was already well developed was lending English engineers to the project to organize and to instruct. Brita Sofia was not slow to realize what benefits associating with such skilled people would confer on her children. She had taught them to read, she had told them stories, but they would soon need more substantial fare.

Or was it Olof Ericsson, instead, who seized every opportunity the canal project's diverse languages, skills and experiences afforded to educate his children? The question later became a bone of contention between the brothers.

When, many years later, Nils was honored with election to the Royal Swedish Academy of Sciences, he wrote a brief autobiographical account for the members, as was the custom. "Since the especially unfavorable economy from 1806 to 1811 had placed my parents in the most straitened circumstances," he wrote in December, 1845, "my father sought and obtained employment as supervisor of rock-blasting workers on the Göta Canal, where he remained from 1811 to 1814. During that time," Nils related, "both I and my brother John...received no other education than what our mother was able to provide."[2]

Nils' autobiographical statement only became known to John Ericsson some years after his brother's death. John Ericsson angrily repudiated Nils' account. "I regret that my late brother's memory will suffer," he wrote, but Nils had "failed in respect for a lovable and just father."[3]

Olof was an educated man, John wrote, and determined to recruit tutors, formal or informal, for his children on any basis he could arrange. When he could not pay, he proved willing to barter for their lessons in mechanical drawing, chemistry, Latin grammar, or French, drawing on the multiplicity of skills the project had drawn from all over Sweden to canalside.[4]

Olof persuaded the chief of the canal headquarters' big drafting room to let the boys draw there. "Thus I secured the opportunity in the year 1811," John remembered, "to make my first drawing to scale. I was also enabled to learn the art of drawing maps, and by the end of the year 1812 could make a pretty accurate drawing, had an excellent knowledge of drawing instruments and was well skilled in their use. ... Our indefatigable father succeeded in persuading the greatest mechanical draughtsman at that time in Sweden, Lieutenant Brandenburg, of the Mechanical Corps of the Navy, to teach us the modern art of shading or finishing off of mechanical drawings. ...

"On one of his visits... Lieutenant Brandenburg was accompanied by the skillful Captain J. Edström, just returned from England. This warm-hearted man took such a liking to Brandenburg's pupils that he advised our father to take us, without loss of time, to Count [von] Platen [director of the canal project] and show him our little works. The great man... encouraged us with many kind words, and in a few months the boys Nils and John Ericsson were appointed cadets in the Mechanical Corps of the Swedish Navy."[5]

Olof had inspired his son John by his fascination with science and engineering and his admiration for Christopher Polhem. This was indelible: all his life John would cherish that inspiration and remain his father's loyal partisan. Nils, on the other hand, from an early age joined Brita Sofia's party, whose doctrine was that Olof had proven himself a lovable loser.

But Count von Platen transformed the lives of both the Ericsson boys. He was, electrifyingly, a winner. Von Platen had himself created the canal project, this new world that now surrounded them, materializing an idea of Polhem that Olof had only dreamed about.

Men felt drawn to him, sometimes against their will, a contemporary wrote, describing von Platen's "iron will and forcefulness in action." These vivid qualities had been developed over a highly unusual life.

Count Baltzar Bogislaus von Platen was the son of an aristocrat who, at his son's birth, was a field marshal and the governor-general of the then-Swedish province of Pomerania, on the eastern shore of the Baltic Sea. At age 13 young Baltzar had embarked on the military career marked out for him by his father, enrolling in Sweden's leading military academy. By 16 he was a lieutenant but realized that Sweden's navy could offer junior officers little exercise of the nautical skills that led to advancement, so he took official leave to become an ordinary seaman in Swedish merchant ships. His merchant voyages took him to many countries, including Morocco and the West Indies and around the Cape of Good Hope.

The war that Sweden fought in 1788 with Russia brought von Platen back on active naval duty. In the sea battle of Hogland he was wounded by shrapnel, and when his warship surrendered he became a prisoner of the Russians, who confined him in Volodimir, Tver and Nishni Novgorod. But during his confinement Sweden continued to advance him in rank.

Once he returned to Sweden in 1790 he was soon commanding vessels of war. Even though admired and influential, he was constantly embroiled in controversy with his superiors. At last, in frustration, he retired from the Navy in 1800.

He meant to practice new methods of agriculture on an estate, Frugården, he had purchased in Sweden. He became a model farmer but then a side-interest seized his entire attention: the project to build a canal "from sea to sea." Von Platen first joined a group of canal enthusiasts. He soon found himself making a more serious study of the terrain than they, and researching through past proposals, and traveling to other countries, including Holland and England, to see how the new canals were being built.

At the end of his study tour he wrote a canal proposal that he presented to King Gustaf IV Adolf not very long before the monarch was deposed, but just in time to receive royal approval and the funds to carry out a survey of the proposed route.

In the 1809 revolution that led to Gustaf's departure von Platen was not only adroit enough to find a political role among the new ruling junta but also to obtain advancement to the rank of admiral.

His arguments for his proposed canal seemed both strong and timely. With Sweden's recent loss of Finland and all its eastern territories surrounding the Baltic Sea (including Pomerania, his family home) the Swedes faced a new vulnerability. Stockholm, on the Baltic, was now transformed into a border town halfway down a thousand-mile poorly defended coastline. The canal he was proposing would be not only commercially advantageous (bypassing the straits where Denmark exacted tolls) but also strategically decisive, giving the Swedish warships in the Baltic an inland passage to the North Atlantic Ocean that would flank the Danish cannon controlling the narrow mouth of the Baltic.

These arguments convinced the interim ruler, Gustaf's brother, to approve arrangements for financing the immense construction. And when the French field marshal, Bernadotte, was named the successor to the Swedish throne, von Platen gained the prospective monarch's wholehearted support.[6]

He would need it. Despite his study of all previous canal proposals and his observations abroad and the advice he solicited from the most famous Dutch and English canal builders, Baltzar von Platen calamitously underestimated both the time and the money it would take to complete the Göta Canal across Sweden. He estimated it would take 10 years to complete, but he was dead by the time, 22 years later, when the great canal was completed.

But that outcome lay far ahead on the day when Admiral Count von Platen welcomed Olof Ericsson and his sons to his office and praised the boys' drawing work in words that John said, more than half a century later, he had never forgotten.

"Continue as you have begun," Baltzar von Platen said to John, "and you will one day produce something extraordinary."[7]

NOTES

1.Goldkuhl, Carola, 1961, 17-22. Lindwall, Gustaf, 1937, 25-29.
2. Ericson, Nils. *Undertecknads Lefnadshändelser* .[Events of My Life] 1845. Facsimile from 7-page original document at Center for History of Science, The Royal Swedish Academy of Sciences, Stockholm. Note that extant personnel records of the Göta Canal project indicate that the terminal year Nils cited for Olof's employment is erroneous; Olof was on the canal project payroll until 1817, not 1814.
3. Goldkuhl, Carola 1966, 80.
4. Church, William C., 1906, i, 17.
5. Church, 1906, i, 15.
6. Ekström, Gustaf, 1938, 9-13, 66-8, 74-5, 78-81.
7. Church, 1906, i, 19.

CHAPTER 9

Whatever his faults as an estimator, Baltzar von Platen demonstrated a firm understanding of the human resources that his project, unprecedented not only in cost but also in duration, would require. Soon after receiving royal approval of his plan, he dispatched two of his best Swedish engineers, Edström and Lagerheim, to England. Earlier von Platen had consulted the most famous English canal builder, Thomas Telford, and brought him to Sweden to survey the canal's proposed route. In England, Lagerheim and Edström received nine months of training under the close supervision of Telford.[1]

On their return, the two engineers became instructors of others. Sweden then had no technical training schools. Telford had easily convinced von Platen that, beyond its immediate training needs, a project of this duration would need to train a younger generation.[2] Soon after, Nils and John Ericsson sported the military uniforms of von Platen's newly formed "Navy Mechanical Corps."

Later, looking back, Nils would complain that "even at an early age I often experienced the obstacles that deficient education placed in my way. As a youth I was forced to grope forward by practical experiments and improvisations of all kinds toward knowledge or goals which would have been much quicker and much surer to achieve if I had ever received a theoretical foundation."[3]

Yet his brother's attitude was opposite. When a friend of John's once remarked, "'It is a pity you did not graduate from a technological institute,' the inventor replied, 'No, it was very fortunate. Had I taken a course at such an institution I should have acquired such a belief in authorities that I should never have been able to develop originality and make my own way in physics and mechanics. ...The want of learning of which my brother complains I never felt, probably because I devoted all my leisure hours to study, while he was occupied with society.'"[4]

The "Navy Mechanical Corps" training was not theoretical, it is true. In his autobiography Nils describes spending four summers of hard physical work on the canal, from mixing the mortar and building the stone walls of locks to cutting down trees and putting them through the sawmill for the massive timbers which would become the lock gates. In the long Swedish winters he says he worked in the drafting room preparing hand-drawn copies of the construction plans and topographical profiles. All of this, indoors and out, was done under Edström's supervision, and Nils grew to value his mentor's attention highly. His account conveys his dismay when, in 1818, Edström left the project "and at 16 years of age I was left without any other direction or training than my own."

Count von Platen had directed that documents and drawings describing "all the existing experience of the canal's construction in Sweden be collected and made available to those young men who wished to profit by them." By hard study there, Nils managed to gain sufficient knowledge to begin mapmaking and "leveling" (mastering the plans and profiles, their dimensions and calculations and then, on site, with the help of an optical instrument, keeping the diggers going in the planned direction to the planned depth as their work progressed). These more technical aspects of the canal work alternated with his physical labors and gradually brought Nils a most thorough knowledge of every aspect of canal building, which would later be of enormous benefit to him.[5] Not least, it equipped him to make realistic schedules and budgets.

Later, as the director of a series of other important canal projects, Nils not only met schedules but even completed projects under budget, performances that made him the leading candidate to organize the construction of Sweden's new railroad system.

In contrast with Nils' summer-long labors in actual construction, John had spent no more than six weeks helping with the stones and mortar and the timbers and then, either because his talent in mechanical drawing was so exceptional or because such talent was in short supply, he spent most of his time, winter and summer, in the drafting room until, in 1816, at age 13, the chance to become an assistant leveler took him outdoors. Within a year he had been given the salaried job of leveler, guiding the sweating labors of 600 shovel-wielding soldiers, except for the soldier following him about with a little stool upon which he had to mount in order to sight through the leveling glass![6]

But Nils was training himself for a career of meeting and surpassing others' expectations, as Brita Sofia counseled him to do, while John was preparing, though he hardly knew it yet, for the occupation Olof Ericsson most admired – that of an inventor.

A mill owner who was well acquainted with both young men at this time and exchanged letters with them later has recorded his contrasting impressions of them:

"Their temperaments were enormously different. John, who was daring to an extreme, especially strove for physical strength. Nils was, on the other hand, all his life very anxious to be well-regarded and, in his younger days, especially anxious to guard his natural good looks. Just at that time [as a worker on the canal] ... he was especially attentive to his superiors and outstandingly cooperative, dependable and punctual in fulfilling his duties – Nils had little physical courage but more true moral courage, based on real deliberation and experience – he was ambitious but honest and genuine."[7]

Both young men had an unusual share of Count von Platen's attention. He had taken a liking to the Ericssons. Anna Carolina Ericsson, their older sister, had been brought into the director's household as a companion to his daughter. It must have been especially difficult for von Platen to see Olof's name appear on the list of those who, because the canal project was again short of money, would have to be dropped from the canal's employment.

The runaway costs of the canal project had come under fire in the Swedish parliament in 1812 and 1815 and again in 1817, when von Platen warned the legislators: "The work simply *cannot* be abandoned, otherwise the Göta Canal will become the most extensive ruins any country has ever yet produced!"[8]

"For lack of knowledge, if nothing worse, you have to mistrust someone who has made a cost proposal of 1,600,000 riksdollars," a parliamentarian shot back, "when you have already added up costs of 3,000,000."[9]

But von Platen rose to such challenges. A contemporary described his mode of speaking: "Outwardly he was rude, often abrasive; but the gallant spirit that animated him, combined with his honesty and unselfishness, gave him a noble and awe-inspiring bearing. Men felt drawn to him, sometimes against their will. He was not eloquent by the usual aesthetic standards, his voice did not ring, his sentences seemed heavy and complicated, but nevertheless he had a kind of eloquence that captivated by brilliance and the strength of his arguments. It was not unlike a gloomy thundercloud shot through with lightning bolts that illuminated or shattered."[10]

Another parliamentarian said "You have to have heard him and seen him... how he began without the least sign of passion; how, as his thoughts developed his arguments piled up higher and higher, the heat of his arguments more and more burst into flame, the flames spread wider and wider and, at last, like a volcano erupting, he struck all one's senses with consternation and awe."[11]

But even the awful eruption of von Platen's eloquence did not suffice this time, and Olof was among the large number of employees who had to be let go in 1817.

However, it is said that von Platen himself intervened to find Olof work. What he found, unhappily for Olof's family, was a job on an island far to the south. A quarantine station for the whole Swedish nation was to be built on the island called Känsö, near the port of Gothenburg, and Olof was given a responsible position in this construction project. But even if the income earned at canalside by Brita Sofia and the two boys had not been indispensable, they could not accompany him: the island had no housing for families. Olof had to leave his family behind.

Only months later, the family got word that Olof had fallen ill. He was suffering from what was called "dropsy," edema, probably caused by heart disease. Brita Sofia left the canal canteen in other hands, and went to Känsö to nurse her husband. But in September 1818, only 40 years old, Olof died.[12]

The terrible news came in a letter from Brita to her son Nils. She asked him to tell Anna Carolina and John.

Oh, what a stab in my breast... John wrote to his mother.

"Last night Nils came from Linköping where he had been at Sister's and told her about our revered Papa's passing away from us, and trying to console her the best he could. And when he came here at night he did not talk about what had happened, but in the morning when we woke up he told me to read the letters [sic] he had received from you but O what a stab in my breast when I saw that Papa was dead, I could never have imagined such a calamity could happen, for both your future and Sister's are now clouded but O if we could help you, Mama, it would be our greatest wish in the world, yet we cannot do so now so we hope to be able to some day. Last night I woke up right in the middle of the night and then could not sleep for thinking over and over of Papa. God alone knows how painful it is that Papa has left us – but we should console ourselves that by the grace of God we may meet and talk again in a better world. Nils' sorrow and mine are more bearable, for we have to keep our minds on other things, but when we have finished our work day it is quite dark and painful, but it is even harder for Sister for she hasn't so much else to distract her thoughts. Your own sorrow I do not want to describe that continually surrounded Papa on his death bed for it must be indescribable. Dear sweet Mama, do not mourn our beloved and revered Papa too much because with the help of God he is numbered among the blessed. Dear Mama, write as soon as you can to us so that we will know what your prospects are or what the Major is arranging for your benefit, for until we know we will not be able to rest. Dear Mama, I have no more time to write this time because I just came home from leveling and now I'm tired and sleepy but I remain until death,
Your beloved and obedient son,
J; [*sic*] Ericsson
P.S. Now at last I think I will have time to visit Sister and try to console her in our great sorrow, which is the best reason in the world, but it will not do to burden our hearts too much. Nils asks me to greet and bless

you. Dear Mama, forgive me for writing so badly and for organizing my thoughts so poorly."[13]

Brita Sofia, newly widowed, was encouraged by the canal administration to resume the management of the canal canteen, a great convenience for the administrators and engineers. But the canteen was not making its expenses. However, when they granted her a monopoly on brewing spirits that she could serve with her meals, at last she could earn enough to pay off some debts. "Nobody can now insult me," she wrote to John, "by reminding me that they have suffered loss of money through my husband."[14]

Her remark was quoted more than a half century after. John Ericsson was relating, with unmistakable irony, that the debts his mother paid off were actually the same she herself had incurred by setting a finer table in the canteen than her husband could afford or the customers would pay for.

Perhaps it was to declare his independence that John decided two years later, at age 17, that he would leave the canal project and enter military service.

The times had invested a military career with more than usual glamour. This was true even in Sweden, which had recently lost so much of its territory through the ill- considered military adventures of King Gustaf III and his son Gustaf IV Adolf that the Baltic Sea had been transformed from a Swedish lake into a threat to the thousand-mile Swedish coastline.

Not just the military's shiny trappings, but their chance for rapid advancement, for a giddy ascent from relative obscurity to power and fame like Napoleon's, had seized the imagination of every enterprising young European. Every enterprising young Swede might further be tempted by the example of Sweden's own Crown Prince, Jean Baptiste Jules Bernadotte, the son of a provincial lawyer, whose military prowess had made him first a marshal in Napoleon's army and then the successor to the Swedish throne, which he ascended as King Karl XIV Johan in 1818, the same year Olof Ericsson died.

Or it might be that Olof's death had lifted from John the burden of fulfilling his father's dream, after Christopher Polhem, of "uniting sea with sea." Like Nils, John Ericsson was conscious of the interest and protection of the canal project director, Count von Platen. Without his support, he could hardly have been given the responsibility of a leveler at only 14 years of age. But by now, at 17, John might have become aware that the Count was beginning to make a distinction between them.

Von Platen admired John's technical precocity that might make him, in time, a highly valuable technical specialist. But he had begun to value the breadth of Nils' leadership abilities and social qualities.

Nils had good counsel from Brita Sofia in his attention to the social aspects of advancement. She had some social pretensions, having been the only daughter of a leading citizen of Långbanshyttan. Mine owner Yngström had given her an unusually thorough education for a woman, expecting that she would have social opportunities appropriate to his station. Now this education found its object in coaching Nils' advancement.

John may well have suspected he was being supplanted in von Platen's favor by his more socially facile, more "rounded" elder brother. He would not have relished being outshone. He might also have harbored resentment that von Platen had allowed Olof to be exiled to the distant island Känsö.

An officer, a German named Captain Pentz, may have sparked John's interest in enlisting. He had tutored the young prodigy in "geometry and planimetry" and in the use of the leveling instrument, and they had become good friends. When Pentz heard that there was such a shortage of surveyors in the remote northern provinces that the Army had increased its standard wage rate for this work by half, he told John he was leaving the canal to become a surveyor. John realized that as a leveler on the canal he himself would have qualifications to apply for the surveying certificate, and might be able to follow Pentz into frontier adventure and high wages.

John went to see Count Baltzar von Platen. The young man's special status is underscored by the fact that he brought the news of his decision to the director's home, not his office. He told his patron of his decision to leave the canal and enter the army. He was surprised when the retired military man was unsympathetic to his military ambitions. It is said von Platen even pleaded with him to remain and continue developing his promising technical talents, the canal needed him, "*I* need you!"

But John had studied von Platen's own never-say-die tenacity, which he would later find ample use for. He did not waver in his decision.

Possibly von Platen, who seems to have been truly fond of the young man, had surprised himself by expressing so much personal feeling and was stung when he saw no corresponding show of emotion. He bridled at a mere boy's unexpected stubbornness. Suddenly a "gloomy thundercloud," he told the young fellow that if he was so determined, he could go straight to hell.

The director's wife, overhearing from the next room that he was about to emit more "lightning bolts," deliberately tipped over her sewing table with a crash! Startled, von Platen sprang into the next room to see what had befallen her.

She had diverted his wrath, averted an eruption, and allowed John Ericsson a lucky escape![15]

NOTES

1. Strömbäck, Lars, 1993, 115-120. See also Lindwall, Gustaf, 1937, 31.
2. "In a letter to von Platen in 1814, Telford writes: 'You must make men for your purposes, as I have done.' This was a view von Platen shared." Strömbäck, 1993, 115.
3. Ericson, Nils, 1845.
4. Church, William C., 1906, i, 16-18. See also Lindwall, 1937, 296-7.
5. Ericson, Nils, 1845.
6. Lindwall, 1937, 33.
7. Goldkuhl, Carola, 1966, 83.
8. Goldkuhl, 1961, 22.
9. Mikael Anckarsvärd quoted in Ekström, 1938, 94.
10. Frans Anton Ewerlöf, quoted in Ekström, 1938, 99.
11. Crusenstolpe, quoted in Ekström, 1938, 99.
12. Men in the Ericsson family typically did not live to a great age. Magnus Stadig (1681- 1727) lived 46 years; his son Eric Magnusson (1724-1755) died at 31; and his son, Olof's father, Nils Ericsson (1747-1790) lived 43 years. Now that Olof was dead at 40, both his sons might well have felt "Time's winged chariot hurrying near," though John would live to a surprising 86 and his brother Nils, to 68.
13. Goldkuhl, Carola,1961, 24-5. The original Swedish contains a few misspellings and some grammar faults.
14. Ericsson, John to Hjalmar Elworth, May 23, 1879.
15. Ekström, 1938, 26. More than one account of this showdown between Ericsson and his patron exists, but Ekström's is the most detailed, even though he misapprehends that Nils had also decided to leave; thus he reports that von Platen's clever wife saved the day for both. Nils, though, remained in the canal project to become, over time, von Platen's most trusted aide, a station chief, an administrator, a manager and, eventually the director of other canal projects of greater commercial value that he actually brought in on time under budget. See also Goldkuhl, 1961, 28.

CHAPTER 10

From the mountainous frontier province of Jämtland, the young soldier wrote letters home. One of these was to his former employer and patron. We know by its tone that Admiral von Platen had soon forgiven the young man's insurrection.

"Drill ought to be arranged," John wrote to the veteran commander, "with the needs of war in mind, and not merely with reference to triumphs on the parade ground.[1] Such parade-ground triumphs do not especially appeal to me. Nothing harms an army's readiness for battle so much as this empty and body-numbing training that does not seem to have any other purpose than to make the service repulsive."[2] They exchanged several letters and the retired seafarer followed John's entry into military life with what might have been a nostalgic interest.

John was also writing to his mother.

"Now we have finished our seven-week-long regimental maneuvers. During this time I have pretty thoroughly experienced what it means to be a military man and this has confirmed for good my liking for the military profession."

John reported that his colonel had promised to ask for his advancement to officer's rank. "...He explained, too, that he wants me to take the surveyor's examination this winter. So, no matter what the state of my resources, this winter I will have to travel to Stockholm. The expenses of the trip will pinch, for I must also buy instruments." Also, he said, an officer's uniform would soon "be official," and he detailed the various items he would have to buy for his new role: "a green coat with epaulettes, new uniform trousers, epaulettes for my tailcoat...a new saber...a sash..."[3]

He thought he could handle most of these expenses, but if Brita Sofia could spare 50 riksdaler, that would help. He was embarrassed to have to ask for it, he said, and he was pained that "even at my age [18] I have to depend on my mother for help so often, a mother who has to save every penny.

"And yet Mama's heart *feels no sacrifice is too great when it is for my children...* " he wrote. "O! What a joy to have a mother who thinks like that."

John's colonel was as good as his word; the young man was advanced to officer's rank on November 5, 1821. His mother's heart must have responded, too, for he made his winter trip to Stockholm and received his surveyor's certificate in 1822. His assignment in Jämtland took him to the remote northwestern part of his country, adjoining the Norwegian border. He joined a corps of surveyors participating in "*avvittring*," a complex process of agricultural land reform that had begun in the mid 18th century and has continued almost into our own era. In early times Swedish agriculture had been based on frontier village mutuality, the arable land divided into small equal plots separately owned but worked in common. However, in the end, some farmers held inherited title to scores of widely separated small plots, a crazy quilt that grew more complex as it grew less efficient to farm. "*Storskifte*," the great shift or exchange, was devised early in the 19th century to amalgamate the multitude of separate small holdings into larger tracts that would be more efficient for individuals to own and work. Such an exchange, if it were to be done fairly, required a precision in devising and revising boundaries that had not hitherto been applied to the frontier lands -- that is, it required skilled surveyors.

So remote was Jämtland from the centers of Swedish population, and so arduous was this precise outdoor work in a subarctic climate and a mountainous terrain, that a 50% premium on the wages usually paid to surveyors in Sweden had to be added as an incentive.

John Ericsson must have been good at it; it is said that he was entered in the records of the organization under two different names, simply to account for his extraordinary production of contour maps, at piecework rates. So the 19-year-old survey officer soon had a lot of money to spend. This sudden onset of prosperity, after years of meager wages as a canal leveler, may have played its role in a style of life that can only be described as "exuberant."

Though producing maps enough for two ordinary surveyors, he also found time to try various schemes to earn still more. He made drawings of canal building scenes featuring accurate technical details from his notes and his memory; their graphic quality made them commercially salable. To carry out a planned series of canal etchings, he invented a gravure machine.[4]

He was a good looking fellow with money in his pocket. He found his new surroundings refreshing and inspiriting, and his social life expanded. He was popular with his men and among his fellow-officers. He began to have a wide acquaintance, both male and female.

But the explosive pace of his activity may also bespeak a release of long-pent pressure. He had made good his escape.

No longer was he the object of Brita Sofia's criticism for "dreamy" speculations on science and invention. She may have blamed this "dreaminess" in her husband Olof for the family's swift loss of fortune, back in Långbanshyttan. In their mother's eyes, older brother Nils' steady diligence may well have become the yardstick for John's performance. Now he had left Nils' invidious example behind him.

Through the years of canal work, John had received Baltzar von Platen's encouragement, but the price of his attention may well have been unvarying concentration on canal-building matters. But by this time John's interest may have begun to flag.

Joining sea with sea was a grand concept, but for a youth who had scarcely even seen the sea, it looked very much like ditch-digging. The canal dream passed down by father Olof from his hero Polhem may have come to seem like a trap, in young John's mind, especially hearing of some doubt among Sweden's parliamentarians that the endless ditching would ever "hold water."

He was a free-spending young fellow in uniform, whose work took him from town to town in Jämtland, so it might have been inevitable that he would find favor with a girl in every town. He began to gain a certain notoriety as "the charming Lieutenant Ericsson." The lore of where he had lived and whom he had courted persisted in local memory for decades after he had left Jämtland and Sweden.

Eventually a surveying assignment brought him to a settlement called Oviken. There, across the lake from the town of Östersund, he rented rooms in a house owned by a retired military officer, Jakob Georg Lilliesköld.

Captain Lilliesköld and his wife had three daughters and pretensions to the nobility – a combination so costly that they were forced to take in a lodger.

Carolina, the youngest daughter, became the object of John's attention. Like many another, she responded warmly. Was she just another score on his card of easy conquests? They say that "the charming lieutenant" was so smitten with Carolina that he applied to her father for her hand.

Captain Lilliesköld is said to have contemptuously rebuffed John Ericsson: "No, she is not for you, a *commoner* with *no future*."

With a curl of his lip, the pretentious captain had targeted John's two deepest fears, the abysses that rimmed his path: early, untimely death that had snatched away his father Olof, his grandfather Nils, his great-grandfather Eric, and Eric's father Magnus; and the ignominious poverty that had grazed his life in Långbanshyttan.

Here, a savage irony intervenes. After Ericsson left, probably evicted for his presumption by Lilliesköld, it was discovered that Carolina was pregnant, and Lilliesköld's next move ensured that his daughter would have a bleak future indeed. He sent her all the way to Stockholm to give birth to John's child in secret, quite possibly never to return.

Did John know that Carolina had been sent a long way from Jämtland? Surely she would have sent him word. Probably he came to Stockholm to see her in whatever secret refuge her parents had arranged for her pregnancy; there is a good possibility that he was in Stockholm in late 1824, when Hjalmar was born, since the records of his regiment say he was on leave from his unit for travel to Stockholm, among other places.[5]

Could they have planned to marry? Serious problems stood in their way. As his wife with or without their child[6] Carolina could only return to Jämtland in defiance of her parents, her very marriage to a commoner a reproach to their aristocratic pretensions. But only in the province of Jämtland could John be sure of earning a relatively good wage; reassigned anywhere else he would make a normal surveyor's wage, one third less money. Romantic inclination and his natural daring must have warred with his still painful recollection of Långbanshyttan, when the auctioneer's hammer fell and fell:

Gone! Gone! Gone!

Not so easily could he return to the province of penury.

He had long been keen to become an inventor. Inventors were the astronauts of this era, heroes exploring the frontiers of mechanical science. In the early age of steam, these explorations were carried out at some risk of life and limb. Olof had related with admiration how Christopher Polhem had risen from the humblest station, through invention, to wealth, fame and the trust of the Swedish king. Perhaps John's inventive abilities could earn the income he and Carolina Lilliesköld needed to marry. He began to experiment in a little workshop he had set up. It was not long before he had devised a pump he thought would raise water out of flooded mines (remembering one cause of Olof's misfortune).

Another of these inventions was an engine that seemed to have very great potential. By the combustion of wood, air alone was heated and air's expansion and contraction was made to drive the "caloric" engine. The principle seemed more economical of fuel and considerably less dangerous than the now widely used steam engine. Such an invention, if it scaled up successfully, could be applied to as many and varied tasks as the steam engine had been. The trouble was that Sweden was only nearing an industrial revolution. England was where the action was.

Years before, when his family had come from Långbanshyttan to the great canal project, English engineers were among the patrons of his mother's refectory. They had been sent from England to apply the lore of superior English technology to the Swedish project. Both John and Nils had been admiring eavesdroppers to their technical chat at table.

Now he had made a little working model of his engine. If only he could take it to England! Should he find backers there, he could patent it and sell the idea. This would make a future with Carolina possible. The dream was tantalizing, but only a dream. Where would he get the money to make such a trip? And would the Army give him leave from his surveying duties?

But it was a persistent dream. Sooner or later, he mentioned his hopes among his fellow surveyors.

Many years later, F.U. Gussander, who had been one of his fellow officers in Jämtland, wrote John Ericsson reminiscing about a favor he had done the young inventor.

"I became more and more obsessed with the idea that this genius should not be buried in Jämtland, and when I heard that he had become involved with a poor girl I considered that he would be lost to the world if he should marry her.

"Then I said to him: Lieutenant, you must travel to England.

"He answered sourly: ...Why do you wake this idea that has slept so long in my imagination, when you know that I do not have the means to do it?

"I answered: How much would you need to travel immediately?

"If I had 1,000 riksdaler I would leave in two weeks.

"Then I took out a loan form and asked him to make it out to himself for this sum, I countersigned it and sent it off...and 14 days later I received the cash..."[7]

With his most unlikely wish granted, Ericsson now needed a year's leave of absence. He applied to his commanding officer, Colonel J.F. Boy. Col. Boy was not only remarkably friendly to the ambitions of his subordinate but was also remarkable in the quality of his friends. Granting Ericsson his leave, he also wrote two letters on the young inventor's behalf.

One was a letter of introduction to the president of a large company at Höganäs, Sweden, that might have a use for Ericsson's inventions in its planned expansion. Boy may have invested in this project himself. The other was to a highly placed Swedish officer asking him to introduce young Ericsson, when he came to Stockholm, to England's minister to Sweden.

The object of all this kind admiration must have found it difficult to say farewell to such good friends, but it is clear he only meant to leave them for one year.

Only halfway through his year in England, Ericsson confirmed his original intentions in a letter to Colonel Boy. He had heard nothing from the Höganäs company, but hoped that the colonel would call on him if this project showed any sign of life, "since no matter what happens I wish to see my homeland again at mid-year..."[8]

During Ericsson's year in England the colonel did not detect any interest at Höganäs in the young man's proposal. Yet Ericsson's wishes must have altered by June, 1827, when he wrote to Boy asking for release from Swedish military service, so that he could continue a big new project he had started. "Lt. Ericsson writes to me from London," Boy told a correspondent, that if he succeeds as he expects in building a massive pump to drain a mine "he will soon be seeing his homeland again."[9] It would not be the last time John entertained such hopes of return to Sweden.

Now, still in Sweden's far north, Ericsson packed up his belongings and also his small working model of the "caloric engine," said goodbye to his many friends, and started south in the beginning of April.

He seems to have arrived in Stockholm late in the month. He may well have visited Carolina Liliesköld there, and made her promises he thought he could keep. He may have gone to see some high official of the company at Höganäs. We know for sure that he paid a visit to General Bloomfield, the English minister to Sweden. There, he met Count Adolf Eugen von Rosen, a Swede several years older and much his elder in experience, who was also en route to England, where he had excellent contacts.

On May 3, John Ericsson's last evening in Stockholm, there was great excitement, cannons roared and bells pealed. The first prince had been born to Sweden's new royal house: King Karl Johan, the former French field marshal Bernadotte, now had a son and heir. Many a *skål* was raised and downed, and John Ericsson must have witnessed the general merriment.

But his thoughts may have turned to another son, his own Hjalmar, for whom there had been no celebration at all.

NOTES

1. Grip, Elias, 1920, 32.
2. Runvik, Margaretha, 1996, 37-8.
3. Lindwall, Gustaf, 1937, 42-4.
4. Church, William C., 1906, i., 31.
5. Brugge, Bengt, 1989, 46-49.
6. Noted in the records of Stockholm's Hedvig Eleonora church is Hjalmar's birth on Nov. 16, 1824, to an "unknown mother aged 19 years," whose father is not named. Hjalmar was given away soon after birth to someone, perhaps a farmer; how long he remained there, no one knows. But Carolina's conscience could not rest and eventually she wrote to John's mother telling her where

the boy was. Brita Sofia is thought to have sent Nils to rescue the child, and herself undertaken to mother him. See Carola Goldkuhl, 1961, 57.
7. Gussander, F.U. to John Ericsson, Dec. 1867, in Lindwall, 1937, 54-6.
8. Ericsson to J.F. Boy, Jan. 4, 1827, in Lindwall, 1937, 71.
9. Boy to Wirsén, July 16, 1827, in Lindwall, 1937, 72.

CHAPTER 11

John Ericsson arrived in the port of Gothenburg early in May, 1826. It would not have taken him long to find a ship going to England, but while he awaited his departure, Ericsson probably strolled around to see the sights in this famous city where he had never been.

He might have gone to see the Trollhättan Canal where it entered the Gothenburg harbor, which was its outlet to the North Sea. This westernmost section of the Göta Canal had been completed in 1822, while Ericsson was far away surveying in Jämtland, and by now the canal was conveying vessels to and from Sweden's great central Lake Vänern. The eastern section where he had worked so many years would not, though, be completed until 1832.[1]

Humble fishing huts fringed the port. The town, whose population was approaching 20,000, had begun as a fishing harbor but when its utility as a cargo link with Europe was recognized, more ambitious development followed. Traders from other nations were encouraged to come and settle there. Now the town had a German church and, just completed the year before Ericsson's visit, a new cathedral replacing one destroyed by fire.

Linnaeus (Karl von Linné) had once described Gothenburg as "the prettiest town in the kingdom." It was ringed with walls and moats when "the king of flowers" visited and was received with cannonades, parades and other high honors. The world- famous Swedish scientist also wrote that it was "divided by regular, straight and level streets, cut through by several waterways that have streets on both sides. ... The bridges and crossings are vaulted, and leafy trees planted on both sides of the waterways. ... The houses are mostly large and heavy wooden structures two stories in height, close together, painted red or yellow but with white or blue corner boards and window frames. ... The Göta River lies close to the town and is connected with the waterways, but on the west a bay of the sea approaches the town, so that large ships can come 3 to 6 miles from the town and there find a convenient and safe harbor. ..."

The town is the seat of the provincial governor, and has a high school, a garrison, a naval unit, fortresses with artillery, two mayors, a pretty town hall with an exchange, two churches and the East India Company. Convenient access by sea from the west without having to pass through the Öresund straits [into the Baltic] facilitates trade... The town is full of people, buyers and sellers, sailors, soldiers, strangers and those who stream there from the whole country... so that the inhabitants thrive and possess fine and handsomely furnished houses. The Lion and the Crown fortresses lie each on its hill."[2]

When Ericsson visited in 1826, the fortresses still stood on their hills, but the medieval walls and gates that once connected them were gone. The frowning towers had been degraded to mere storehouses. The inhabitants had thrived so expansively in the 18th century that the king granted their petition to raze the ancient walls in 1807.[3] When that king was deposed and the time of troubles came in 1809, with Russian troops occupying northern Swedish towns and other enemy armies mustering in east and south, the inhabitants had reason to regret this. However, by Ericsson's visit in 1826, a peaceful Gothenburg's port was welcoming ships from all over the world. It is said that on a typical day hundreds of sailing ships could be seen at anchor there, a forest of masts. No steamships would regularly connect Gothenburg with England until 1843.[4]

Among the clutter of islands off the entrance to Gothenburg's port was one that John Ericsson may have longed to visit. Känsö, where his father Olof had briefly worked and died and been buried in 1818, must have seemed tantalizingly near. But it had become a quarantine station, where he would not be allowed ashore.

Perhaps Ericsson spent no time on sightseeing. He expected to be returning in a year, and he was eager to begin his expedition. Perhaps, on the very day he arrived, he and his baggage were rowed out into the harbor to a ship making ready to sail for England. It would have been no small coaster, though there were some at anchor there, but a proper tall ship, able to cross the turbulent North Sea.

Besides his clothing and papers, he was bringing an invention, a working model of a "heat engine." Inside it, a fire of wood would heat the air, whose alternate heating and cooling provided the energy to do mechanical work, more cheaply and safely than the steam engines that were catalyzing an industrial revolution, especially in England. He hoped that his demonstration of this device would attract English backers, who would finance the patenting of it and its manufacture. He had packed this working model in a sturdy wooden box.

John Ericsson, powerfully built and athletic, would have had no trouble managing this box, but on the thwart of the ship's boat it may have crowded him and the rest of his baggage. Though, even for a year abroad, the young surveyor may not have had so much of a wardrobe to bring.

But he was bringing along another kind of baggage. There was, first of all, his rage over his rejection by Carolina's parents when he asked to marry her. We know from his fellow-officer Gussander's reminiscence that Ericsson was nevertheless still thinking of marriage: "I considered... that this genius should not be buried in Jämtland... [and] that he would be lost to the world if he should marry her."

When Gussander made his offer the young inventor's ambition kindled at once. Yes, that was it, he would accept this wonderful chance of a year in England, and then bring the fruits of his success back, to claim his Swedish bride and reclaim his child!

His conscience then allowed him to face Carolina with this plan, to persuade her to wait for his return to Sweden bringing renewed resources. Carolina, already in a strange place and even more frightened at this lonely prospect, knew her family would force her to give the newborn child away before she could return home. She must have been skeptical, yet saw no choice but to accept his fervent vows and wish him well.

Now the boat carrying John Ericsson was rowed out of the shallows for the deepwater anchorage, threading among the looming hulls whose masts and rigging cast a plaid of shadows on the water and among a lively traffic of barges stacked with goods. He was not a spectator at canalside now, this was no single-file review of dream ships through a great ditch of locks filled at last, after all the labors he knew so well, with water. This was a thronged seagoing harbor. The pulse of trade had driven a jostling crowd of vessels here, cargoes were being loaded and unloaded into and out of these wood-and-canvas birds of passage, hoarse cries of direction and of exertion and shrill cries of seagulls wove a glistening net of sound. John Ericsson's own pulse quickened amidst this strange new scene, and when the oarsman conveying him and his baggage shipped his oars and hailed a mate standing up above, on the deck of a three-masted barque, the son of an iron miner stared straight up the 125 feet to the top of its mainmast with awe.

The sailor on deck dropped a line into the boat to secure it and shoved a rope ladder over the railing that fell down within reach of the boat. The oarsman swiftly passed a hitch through an iron ring in the boat. Then he seized his passenger's duffle and heaved it up to his fellow on the deck, who had to stretch out to snatch it at its apogee. The oarsman was reaching for the young inventor's box when John Ericsson threw a rude shoulder and elbow between. Emitting an inchoate warning he clutched the awkward box under one arm. If his precious invention, the vehicle of all his hopes in England, was not to be tossed up in the same perilous way, its owner would have to struggle up a rope ladder one-handed. Even the oarsman was impressed when he managed this, and so made no complaint that his help had been so roughly refused.

Panting, John Ericsson clambered over the railing onto the deck of the sailing ship and set down his box. As he straightened up he felt a hand on his shoulder. He turned to face Adolf Eugen von Rosen, whom he had met in Stockholm a few days before, probably when he called on the English minister to Sweden.[5] Ericsson and von Rosen had been attracted to one another at once. They had soon discovered that they were about to be traveling companions.

Now Ericsson returned the businessman's greeting with enthusiasm. But they would not be neighbors on the ship. To conserve his fixed capital Ericsson would have bought the cheapest ticket he could. The young inventor was concerned over how to safely stow his precious box and other belongings in the shared, perhaps common hammock space down below that he had paid for. He would soon have excused himself and gone below.

The sails swelled, as with a deep breath of resolve: *Away! To England!* And as the wake began to unfurl behind his ship, young John Ericsson gazed back toward the city of Gothenburg in a sudden melancholy.

Back there was Brita Sofia, still energetic, competent, but graying; thank God Nils would be able to attend to her needs and, if she faltered, keep her from want. Nils was already supporting Anna Carolina, their sister. Count von Platen favored Nils and seemed to be grooming him for new duties in the canal project, so John's brother should be able to handle this burden for a year, just a year after all. Nils knew that he would help out, John had promised to contribute just as soon as the returns from his inventions began to come in.

Behind him, too, were his promised bride Carolina Lilieskböld and the infant, now just 16 months old, they had decided to call Hjalmar. How would she manage? Her parents would have to help, that's all. His thoughts hurried on.

He was parting from the military life he had declared suited him perfectly. Colonel Boy, his commanding officer, had instantly understood his ambition. Through a friend, the colonel had helped him secure a year's leave and even arranged for him to meet the English minister when he passed through Stockholm. A year's leave. Leave from everything. To leave his country. Sweden and everything he had ever known in nearly 23 years of life were dwindling, dwindling as the wake widened behind the tall ship taking him to strange shores.

Now he was looking back as they left the Gothenburg harbor mouth where the fortress New Älvsborg crouched, its stone ramparts and central keep still bearing scars of honor from the 1719 repulsion of the Danes. Now, the lighthouse on the island of Vinga, and beside it, the abstractness of its geometry a curious anomaly in this place, a masonry pyramid with a beacon at its tip.[6] He watched these last Swedish things grow less and less, and then he turned sharply away from them and strode the length of the deck, into the bow of the ship.

He took a deep breath. He had embarked at last, he was freed as well as parted. As a boy, infected with a dream that was not his own, he had spent years confined in a dismal ditch calculating the path of a troop of cursing diggers. He had not dared to question Count von Platen's vision of a canal along which stately merchantmen and majestic men o'war were gliding like potent wraiths from sea to sea. Yet as the ditch advanced, year after year still dry but for their sweat, he had felt more and more trapped, with no horizon but its crumbling margins.

But now he was moving like the wind across a shining expanse that seemed to have no limits. In his pocket he had what he thought was a year's freedom to become, like the fabled Polhem, an inventor who would bring new knowledge back to Sweden for his reward.

But limits of which he could have no knowledge lay beyond his horizon: prejudice, jealousy, historic and invincible inertia, indifference and a vengeance that would twice confine him within prison walls.

Yet this sea voyage itself contained the seeds of a fame that would, 36 years later, make his name known in every seagoing country of the world. His life was passing through this brief voyage from Sweden to England as through a prism, from which all the lines of his subsequent 63 years of life would diverge.

Would this son and grandson and great-grandson of iron miners, would the boy who had followed his father Olof down into the lightless corridors where men hacked wealth out of the earth, would John Ericsson ever have invented two great warships, the *Princeton* and the *Monitor*, and a multitude of maritime weapons and devices, if he had not made this voyage?

The voyage itself was more than exhilarating. He was being conveyed over the sea by what he must have quickly realized was one of mankind's greatest inventions, a vessel of ultimate human ingenuity conveyed over hundreds of generations.

He, who had designed a little machine to harness the expansion and contraction of heated air to do work, must have quickly recognized in this ship a mechanism based on a related phenomenon, but millions of times more powerful. It was a mechanism that had been eons in development, a great congeries of inventions and refinements to harvest the wind's invisible but palpable power and put it to work.

Now he studied the sailing ship's components of wood and metal, cloth and rope and human skill, teamwork and muscle, noting how all these were combined and orchestrated to harness the wind's immense resource. Everything in his subsequent life suggests that he was no mere passenger, that John Ericsson became a student of this, his first real ship directly experienced, his eye seeking out and compiling principles of sail and rigging, windlass and rudder, tumble-home and displacement that he would later apply to ships of his own devising.

His new friend Adolf von Rosen, at 29 six years older than he, was equipped by experience to become his mentor in this subject. At age 18, von Rosen had already become a second lieutenant in the Swedish navy, and by Ericsson's present age of 23 the young count had been commissioned a lieutenant in the British navy, experiencing battles with pirates and other adventures that took him as far away as South America.

Recently, von Rosen had been in England looking for ways to make his fortune out of the new English technology, so his encountering John Ericsson was timely. He would introduce the younger man to the Swedish minister and other influential people in London, he would become the inventor's sales agent on the Continent and then his business partner and eventually John Ericsson's best friend for life.

Von Rosen was also equipped by experience to serve the green new arrival in England as an interpreter in the English language. However, Ericsson may not have needed such assistance for long.

He already had his eye on a grander horizon than that encompassed by the Swedish language. Only a matter of months after he arrived in London, he submitted an illustrated technical paper, "A Description of a New Method of Employing the Combustion of Fuel as a Moving Power" to the newly established *Institution of Civil Engineers* in London.[7] The paper had to be translated from his Swedish, but he was going to achieve a remarkable facility with the English language.

Decades later, William C. Church, Ericsson's first American biographer and before that a longtime associate of the inventor, wrote that "his thorough command of English ... was a subject of remark. It could hardly be otherwise ... with a language he had learned in his youth."[8]

Brita Sofia had been a devoted reader of the romances of Sir Walter Scott (possibly in their original language) so Ericsson may have heard his first English words at her knee. The family's relocation to the Göta Canal headquarters at Forsvik when he was 7 years of age insured that the rest of his boyhood would bring him frequently among English-speaking engineers.[9]

Yet Ericsson's sojourn in the English language was also an exile. He subscribed to Swedish newspapers. In correct Swedish, he corresponded with high Swedish officials, latterly including the King himself. As advancing age and incessant labors made his New York social contacts dwindle, he corresponded in Swedish all the more avidly with family members and with his friend and longtime partner von Rosen.

But not without strain: "Overwhelmed with work, I have not had the time to write the description you ask for in my native tongue. ... But this is only the case in mechanical matters, because when the language of the heart is to be used I prefer to express myself in my native tongue."[10]

The language of the heart. He wrote this long after Carolina Lilieskold, despairing of his return, had married another, and his son Hjalmar (to whom he had never yet written in either language) was being raised by his mother, Brita Sofia, and his brother Nils. He wrote this after he had married a young Englishwoman, but then emigrated to America without her, though he supported her the rest of her life and exchanged letters with her, though in English, of course.

It was in Swedish, this 'language of the heart' that in 1876 he wrote a nephew to warn that "A visit from Hjalmar will be unpleasant in many respects."[11]

But even before he knew that his son was en route to America and might come to see him whether it was unpleasant for him or not, he wrote, "I have for a series of years led an eccentric life. I never visit anybody, and never receive visits excepting from a few professional persons. ... In truth, I may be regarded as a stranger, of whom everybody has heard, but whom nobody knows personally."[12]

It was the life that lay ahead of young John Ericsson when he strode eagerly ashore in Hull, England on May 18, 1826.

NOTES

1. Bonsdorff, Leo, 1931, 2. See also Bonsdorff, 1907.
2. von Linné, Karl, July 9-13, 1746, in H. Fröding, 1903, 1-3.
3. *Sverigeboken*, 1982, 118.
4. Bonsdorff, 1931, 2.
5. Lindwall, Gustaf, 1937, 58.
6. Personal communication Sept. 9, 2004 from Christer Olausson, Gothenburg Maritime Museum Library, Gothenburg, Sweden.
7. Personal communication from ICE. A facsimile of the English translation was furnished, though the drawings to which it refers have disappeared. However, a page from the "Minutes of ICE Ordinary Meeting 20 February 1827" was also provided, from which the following is excerpted: "Mr. Carlsund presented some drawings of a plan by Lieut. Ericsson, a gentleman present this Evening, for obtaining a moving power by the agency of heat or flame alone." Adelsköld, C.L., 1894, 30, states that this same paper had been submitted to ICE in 1825, a year before Ericsson set out for England, but it seems unlikely that a paper in the Swedish language would have been sent to England even before Ericsson had made his plans to travel there. Note that the ICE minutes do not mention any working model. The model Ericsson brought to England, tested and demonstrated in Sweden with wood chips, could not

endure the greater heat of English coal, and may well have failed its inventor before the meeting of February 20.

8. Church,1906, i, 223.
9. Church, 1906, i, 12.
10. Church, 1906, i, 32.
11. Ericsson to Baron John Ericson, April 1876, in Runvik, Margaretha, 1996, 144.
12. Ericsson to unnamed correspondent on March 24, 1876, in Church, 1906, ii, 232. The authorized biographer did not always identify Ericsson's correspondent, as here. Since the tone of this self-judgment is ruminative, one wonders if it was a fugitive page from Ericsson's many diaries, all of which he destroyed, to Church's dismay.

III

In New York

CHAPTER 12

When John Ericsson and Hjalmar Elworth met for the second and last time, there is no record of what they said to each other. But clear written records define what Hjalmar brought to the meeting and what he received from John to take back to Sweden. Facts delimit the speculation over their meeting. But they also spur it.

Begin with the facts.

It is September, 1876, in New York City. A traveler whose luggage is dusty with the mingled soils of the North American continent he has just twice traversed arrives at the home of a man who came to the United States in 1839, and became a naturalized citizen of the U.S. in 1848, but has never traveled farther from New York than Washington, D.C., and has not left Manhattan for at least thirty years.

But this is a relationship, not a chance encounter. Begin again.

An illegitimate son enters a house where his biological father awaits his coming. The son is 52 years of age, the father, 73. They have met once before, briefly. This time the son will be his father's guest. But they will not meet again. Not ever.

But there is a context, these are facts with larger dimensions. Once more:

Two Swedes meet again, a middle-aged man about to return to his remote northern land after an absence of several months, and an aged man never to return to that homeland in this life, though he has both longed and feared to do so for more than four decades.

The middle-aged man has been sent to America by the Swedish government under a longstanding program of sending accomplished specialists abroad to study foreign science and engineering for a time and then to bring the fruit of their observations home for use in Sweden.

Fifty years before, this same philosophy of encouraging travel abroad to harvest progress for Swedish use may have helped 23-year-old John Ericsson justify abandoning his son, Hjalmar Elworth, to seize an opportunity to go abroad.

Only one of the men in the room is ever going to bear the fruits of foreign travel home to Sweden. On this day in 1876 Hjalmar has just returned from a swift expedition across North America and back made possible by the very latest technology, the new transcontinental railroad.

When he knocked on the door of No. 36 Beach Street this time, Elworth probably did not again have to wait in line to be admitted, but was received with immediate attention. S.W. Taylor knew by now that Elworth was his employer's son. Ericsson's manservant or housekeeper would have led Hjalmar to guest quarters; this time it would be a visit and not an interview. He would have been invited to wash up and rest and refresh himself until his father, upstairs at his drafting table, came to a stopping point in his work.

Hjalmar may well have had time to think back over the tumultuous weeks that had passed since his first meeting with John Ericsson.

"The sum total of my rail travels," he would report to the Swedish government, "came to 8,275 miles" on 14 different rail lines, "and my travels on lakes and rivers came to 500 miles."[1] *Since July!*

In Philadelphia before these travels, numerous fellow Swedes had shared weeks with Elworth attending the Centennial Exhibition, 14 of them grantees making study-tours of other American industries. Taking leave of them, Hjalmar had set out in the company of Fritz von Dardel. Dardel was a popular Swedish artist and museum administrator, a favorite of the Swedish king, who often sought his advice on renovation and decoration of apartments at the palace. Dardel had come to Philadelphia to serve on the expert jury awarding medals of merit for the best paintings and sculptures displayed in the various national pavilions. He was also a diarist, illustrating charming accounts of his adventures and misadventures with droll cartoons that Swedish newspapers regularly published.

The two men first traveled by rail to Washington, D.C., where the minister of Sweden, Carl Lewenhaupt, and his wife took them out sightseeing in their carriage and then brought them home to dinner. Philadelphia had been very warm; the capital proved to be torrid.

"...Since I longed to refresh myself at Niagara, on the next day I traveled there in Elworth's company," Dardel recorded.

"Our route traversed Baltimore, Harrisburg and Elmira. From there we traveled beside the beautiful Seneca Lake. ... This route is both diverse and full of interest. In Rochester, quite near to Lake Ontario, we stayed over for a day; it is a well built city...

"We arrived at Niagara at 7:00 in the morning. ...It is not until you come to a suspension bridge, which is 1,268 feet long and has a height above the river of 160 feet, that you see the waters ... crash into the deep." The two travelers remained over a weekend to see all the sights both by sunlight and moonlight, captivating the artist, if one can believe the diarist.

"Elworth was now going to travel to California to observe the railroad improvements that have been accomplished there recently," Dardel wrote in his diary. "I would gladly have accompanied him had it been a more favorable season, but in the prevailing heat it didn't appeal to me to sit for eight days straight, shut up in a railroad car. So I took my leave of my splendid traveling companion..."[2]

On the road, Hjalmar Elworth kept a professional travel journal in which he recorded not charming stories, but closely observed details of railroad construction and equipment, even noting there the exact interval between telegraph poles beside the railbed. Details that would have special relevance to Sweden's railroads held his attention:

"Snow blockages occurred so often, at first, in crossing over the Sierra Madre between the Trucke and Emigrant Gap stations where the line is partly blasted into and partly built up along the mountain wall that, in sundry places, it became necessary to build a roof over the track. These roofs were later extended farther and farther until they now constitute one continuous roof between the two stations, 36 miles in length, covering the Summit, Cisco and Emigrant Gap stations as well.

"Such *snowsheds,* which are likewise found along mountain slopes at several points on both the Central Pacific and Union Pacific lines, consist of a long sloping board roof projecting so far out that the track is covered, resting on a beam pinned to a row of vertical posts, usually tree trunks with the bark left on, braced with 3-inch boards and at a distance from each other along the line of 6 feet. ..."[3]

"*Snowplows* are used on the Central Pacific railway on the high plains between the Sierra Nevada and the line's eastern terminus, Ogden, as well as on the Union Pacific and Grand Trunk and other railways. Central Pacific's snowplow is made of timbers and wood-covered, with a length of around 30, a breadth of around 10 and a height of 13 feet; it rests on twin 4-wheel trucks and at the rear is equipped with a braking apparatus. The front end forms a plane with an inclination of 1:1-1/2..."[4]

Much later he would mention to his father building many snowplows for Swedish use from the design of one that had been shown him in San Francisco. As he had done at the exhibition, he procured engineering drawings of such mechanical designs as he judged worthy of report.

Hjalmar was obsessive about continual safety inspection and maintenance of track and roadbed. He would later write his father about his own absences from Stockholm on inspection trips that cost him many days. In his official travel report from America he related the terrible consequences of the lack of such care: "A westbound express train on Union Pacific I was riding on August 24 was halted in the evening at the Medicine Bow station, where we were informed that the freight train of 14 cars coming in the opposite direction...had derailed down a bank that had been washed out by a heavy rain for a length of about 30 feet. The engineer, the fireman and one more man had died instantly, the locomotive was a total loss, and the cars were crushed."[5]

Hjalmar was also noting down the details of organization, the personnel structure and delegation of duties along the line "which, depending on local conditions and the extent of the operation, is divided into divisions of 100 to 300 miles," the composition and functions of executive committees. The president of Pennsylvania Railroad, the vice-president and general manager of the Grand Trunk Railway, the general superintendent of the Union Pacific Railway and the chief engineer of the Central Pacific Railroad are all named in his report and thanked for obtaining the information and materials Hjalmar Elworth wished.

The letter of introduction from John Ericsson must have worked well. If he had come to America wondering whether his father's fame had ebbed, now he was reassured that the Merlin of the *Monitor* had become a permanent presence in American Civil War legend.

When Hjalmar had put his luggage away and dusted off his clothes, he might have returned to the first floor to look around while waiting.

Heavy chandeliers and mantel mirrors lent the rooms "a certain air of old-fashioned dignity, but the handsomely finished and exquisitely polished specimens of [Ericsson's] solar apparatus occupied every corner of the parlor and gave it the appearance of an alcove in the Patent Office. An oil portrait belonging to a friend, a bust of [another friend], an elaborately engraved and framed copy of the resolutions passed by the Legislature of the State of New York on the occasion of the *Monitor* fight, and a portrait of [U.S. Navy Assistant Secretary] Gustavus V. Fox, were the only specimens of artistic adornment displayed about the house."[6]

Sooner or later Hjalmar found himself at table for the very first meal he had ever shared with his father.

Ericsson once described his daily menu in a letter:

"My breakfast consists 365 times a year of two soft-boiled eggs, 2 cups of brown tea, weak and quite sweet, and a half loaf of brown bread made of unsifted cornmeal and wheat flour containing 94 cubic inches per loaf, the passage to the transforming apparatus being eased through abundant grease consisting of fresh butter.

"My dinner consists 365 days a year of [either] roast beef, beef steak or mutton chops, all in small portions, a deep bowl of enough boiled potatoes for four persons, a bowl of spinach or beans and a lesser quantity of assorted vegetables, canned, in wintertime. Afterward, fruit, following which 2 cups of brown tea are taken, weak..., with 6 sugar cubes, each 5/8 inch long, dissolved in each cup. A substantial quantity of butter and brown bread is eaten during this tea-drinking, which concludes my day's diet."[7]

"I have important work before me," Ericsson wrote on another occasion, "and hence live like a man training for a fight. My reward is unbroken health."[8]

Hjalmar Elworth, a veteran of banquets when the King of Sweden led the celebrations opening new railroad lines, may have found the cuisine spartan. But after so much hard travel and with so many issues unresolved, his mind may not have been on the food.

John Ericsson would have greeted his son in their native Swedish. He would have made courteous inquiries about the fatigues of the trip and his son's state of health, asked when he planned to embark and whether he would travel home by way of England or wait for a ship directly to their homeland. Ericsson's Swedish, even after half a century away, was perfectly equal to this kind of conversation. He read Swedish newspapers daily and occasionally conversed with Swedish-Americans who were part of the city's cosmopolitan community, and he carried on a steady correspondence in Swedish with officials in Sweden's Ministry of Naval Defense, family members and others.

While father and son dined, each took the measure of the other. Ericsson may again have noted Hjalmar's striking resemblance to his mother, Carolina Lilliesköld, but also noticed a certain formality or reserve, that Hjalmar might have learned from Nils. John Ericsson would have noted his son's well-made, if now travel-rumpled apparel, thinking that Hjalmar's high executive position, which in Ericsson's view Nils had made possible, gave his son an income many a desperate inventor might envy.

In his own son John would have seen much else of brother Nils, who had been more of a father to Hjalmar than he ever had – Nils' expressions, gestures, mannerisms, possibly even political opinions. Echoes of the forceful personality with whom he, John, had come more and more into conflict until at last his brother, as the self-made Baron Ericson, had declared his independence of their father (or so John interpreted his change of name).

John Ericsson might also have felt some apprehension whether his son would reopen matters he had tried to lock up for good, decades before.

Hjalmar would certainly not have forgotten how "unpleasant in many ways" his father had said a first visit from his son would be. And yet he had offered Hjalmar help in making contacts with high officials and invited him for this second visit.

It would not have been surprising if Hjalmar was looking at his father through Nils' eyes. Nils, the stay-the-course on-track solid citizen and achiever, seemed to see his younger brother's life as a zig-zag from one sidetrack to another:

John, who had begun by wasting his initial advantages just as their father Olof, that dreamer, had. Leaving the great national canal project to enlist in a frontier regiment, progressing to an officer and a surveyor, and yet turning from this promising venture to tinker with inventions. John who, in quest of fame as an inventor, had on impulse borrowed money for an ill-considered visit to England, abandoning all his responsibilities to his aging mother and to his unmarried sister, abandoning his duty to his brother to help support them; leaving the mother of his son, their child dumped into the grudging hands of a farm family. After this visit to England had lengthened into 13 years, John had only two prison terms for debt to show for it. When Nils, helping him out of his difficulties as usual, had urged him to settle down, marry, take a steady job, John had done so, but soon abandoned these responsibilities, too. Lured by the siren Invention he had emigrated to America, where he spent many more years in unsuccess. Only by the accident of a war that had found a fortuitous use for his ingenuity did he at last acquire fame and fortune, but for this he had sacrificed the happiness of others as well as his Swedish identity, culture and language.

Was it entirely through this dark lens that Hjalmar, fostered by Nils, looked at John Ericsson?

Tempting, no doubt, to share his uncle's opinions of everything. Nils was as good a father as Hjalmar ever had. Nils was a national hero, he had helped make the Swedish national railroad a reality and was ennobled by the king for it. But Nils had more than fulfilled what was expected of him, he had lived securely within convention, he was a "regular." He had rescued John's illegitimate son and treated him well, the boy had shared much with Nils' own sons, and his uncle had arranged for Hjalmar's education, employment and advancement. Yet Hjalmar was not quite his son, Hjalmar's family name was a fiction, this was only one of many shades of difference Hjalmar felt but, in the name of gratitude, would have striven not to show. Conformity was his shield and convention, his armor against social disdain as a bastard, and an abandoned bastard, at that. He learned to be a good actor, but he knew deep within he was not "a regular" like Nils any more than his father was.

Thus a gnawing curiosity might have mingled with his acquired view of John Ericsson. What was his father like, what qualities in himself might John Ericsson have authored? These were the simplest of his questions, observation alone might answer them.

But more urgent questions remained. Their first interview had extorted the old man's acknowledgment, in private at least, of his paternity, but Hjalmar's curiosity remained unallayed. Questions that had eaten at him all his life were still unanswered. These questions had brought him back to Beach Street.

And perhaps his fervent wish for a special kind of recognition had brought him back, the wish he had expressed four years before, in his first letter to John Ericsson, to be acknowledged by his father as a technical man like himself, a real professional. Not only recognition that "you are my son," but that "you are a son worthy of your father."

Soon enough, Hjalmar would have brought up the new railroads. He would have been eager to describe the new, transcontinental manifestation of a railroad technology in whose early development in England the inventor himself had taken a dramatic part. He would have described to his father the ingenious features of the new railroad engines, brake systems, passenger car designs and other railroad devices he had studied at the exhibition in Philadelphia and seen at work on the rails across the continent and back.

Doubtless Hjalmar described them in Swedish. The Swedish technical jargon that was his son's workaday instrument might have been unfamiliar to John Ericsson. As far back as 1833, 7 years away from home in London, he had written "I have already forgotten the little I know of our language's scientific terminology."[9] Some 30 years later, Ericsson wrote from New York that "my technical vocabulary [in Swedish] is so meager that I simply cannot say what I want about mechanical things."[10]

In his luggage Hjalmar had a bundle of engineering drawings given him by exhibitors and the officers of the various railways whom he had interviewed; these he would bring home for copying into illustrations for his lengthy travel report when published. Now he would have produced them for the interest of the superb draftsman Ericsson. Looking through this collection together may have been a high point of their conversation, easing the tension between them for the time. It may have been just then that Ericsson showed his son a proof copy of his massive "Contributions" book, with its outstanding technical illustrations, and got Hjalmar's promise to arrange for the volume's translation and publication in Swedish.

Hjalmar's published travel journal never mentioned it, but he must also have seen vast fertile plains, dire deserts and mountains of awe-inspiring height; he would have glimpsed wild herds that filled the horizon, and flocks that darkened the sky. He had rubbed shoulders with every kind of railroad passenger, suited, booted, skirted or befeathered, observing their behavior, to a European often odd and sometimes inexplicable, with interest.

Hearing about all this from Hjalmar may have compelled the attention of the long- ago inventor of the "Novelty" locomotive. Yet at the same time this narrative of colorful curiosities may have been a subtle irritant, reminding the longtime exile from Sweden that he had not really come ashore in his adopted country, but was becalmed somewhere between.

But Hjalmar was achieving what he wanted, a recognition that he was an able technical man. Otherwise his father would hardly be entrusting him with getting *Contributions* translated and published in Sweden. With a fresh breath of self-confidence, the son may now have felt emboldened to bring up some unfinished business between them.

The questions, brooded over all his life by the son, and by the father dreaded for more than half a lifetime:

Why did you let me be given away?

Why did you take no notice of me for 48 years?

Brief questions, but there were only long answers.

Your mother gave you away, she was forced to do it by her parents, otherwise they would not have let her come home. I was not there and I certainly was not consulted, John Ericsson might have responded.

I took what notice of you I could, in the midst of struggling for a living in England, in America, coping with the scheming of others to keep me down, even getting me confined to prison to prevent my inventions from driving theirs from the marketplace. I earned so little for so many years, but whenever I could I sent money to Nils for your support.

Was it neglect that I did not address you directly, Hjalmar, or encourage you to communicate with me? I thought I was doing that for your own good. I felt that if Nils was willing to foster you, yes, to father you, nothing was gained for you by my trying to compete with him from across the ocean. And here you are, the proof of my belief – successful and trusted with important work. How can you say I was wrong?

Long answers, complex explanations, not easy to frame when feelings evaded and repressed for half a lifetime kept rushing out.

Questions in Swedish. Could the father have answered them in a language that although he read and wrote in it almost daily he seldom spoke it and never, never, never expressed such feelings, for such purposes of self-defense, of extenuation? It seems certain that John Ericsson lapsed back into English, where he had the upper hand of his son, his interrogator, however respectful, nevertheless his accuser.

What are the facts? Could these questions really have been asked and answered? Did a reconciliation take place? No one knows. We know only that Hjalmar accepted his father's assignment. His clear official duty on arrival home was to write a lengthy travel report and supervise preparation of its complex illustrations for publication, and meantime to take up again the heavy duties of a director of an expanding national railway.

Never mind, he would help his father get his *Contributions to the Centennial Exhibition* into Swedish hands and minds as the old man dearly wished.

A series of letters between the parties to this agreement exist. They tell us quite a lot.

John Ericsson wrote to his son about this assignment in a cool, demanding tone. Sometimes he expressed harsh impatience with the pace of services he evidently expected Hjalmar to render him on demand. Occasionally he even lectured this railroad executive as if he were an errant schoolboy.

Hjalmar's letters to John Ericsson were unfailingly correct and courteous, even if the warmth and openness of his first letter to his father, signed "Hjalmar," had now given way to a formal tone of respect, with the invariable signature "Hj. Elworth." It is only in the drafts of Hjalmar's letters, several of which have been preserved, that we see the outbursts of impatience, anger and desperation that were a much-crossed-out, spattered and blotted confession that he had feelings he would keep at home.

The handwriting of the emigrant inventor, in his letters to Hjalmar, is notable for its difficulty. It is almost entirely horizontal, every vertical stroke is minimized, a mere blip on the horizon. It is almost as though Ericsson's message to his son was an ironclad concealing two-thirds of its mass below the surface. Whether this vessel was on a mission of attack or defense is hard to judge.

But perhaps not impossible?

NOTES

1. Elworth, Hjalmar, 1876a, 11.
2. Dardel, Fritz von, 1916, 222.
3. Elworth, 1876b, No. 12, 7.
4. Elworth, 1876c, 143.
5. Elworth, 1876b, No. 11, 5.
6. Church, William C., 1906, ii, 312-13. Church called frequently on Ericsson, so these are his personal observations. In the same place he continued "Ericsson never found time for the cultivation of a taste for art, and there was a noteworthy absence in his house of everything appealing to aesthetic sentiment; but the pins in the cushion on his bedroom bureau were always arranged by himself so that they should be in exact mathematical rows. Utility, and not taste, controlled the appointments of his house."
7. Ericsson, John, to Axel Adlersparre, no date given, in Runvik, 1996, 120.

The author continues that Ericsson "said he never ate fish, for it destroyed the brain, nor ever ate soup because it was really rubbish."

8. Church, 1906, ii, 310.
9. Ericsson to Adolf von Rosen, Oct. 11, 1833.
10. Ericsson to Axel Adlersparre, Dec. 24, 1864.

CHAPTER 13

What were these "contributions" John Ericsson made to the 1876 Centennial Exhibition? They began as a "gap" that Ericsson detected in the history of technology in America, as displayed in Philadelphia. To fill this gap, he was engaged in the production of a book so massive that it can almost be called a monument. An illustrated catalog of every one of his inventions since he had arrived in the United States in 1839, it was also a kind of scale model of his entire 37-year American career to date.

He launched it in 1876 at great expense, a kind of golden boat like the one bestowed on him in 1862. But in 1876 he built the tributary vessel himself, and sent it around the world.

The story begins with what must have been an epic humiliation.

"I have *five* times stood before an American jury...and five times the judgment has gone against me" he confided on April 25, 1876 to a Swedish parliamentarian, Axel Adlersparre.

"I will not be taking any direct or indirect part in the Philadelphia exhibition, even though I now possess a whole museum of the most splendid philosophical instruments (built by myself). I have *five* times stood before an American jury – God knows, in all innocence – and five times the judgment has gone against me – this country's scientists are all against me, as are even the engineers, and every one of them, more or less, is a villain."[1]

"Judgment"..."innocence, God knows..." The hammer in Långbans-hyttan falls and falls, sixty-six years later it still passes sentence. And the penalty? As before, banishment.

These are painful matters to communicate, but Ericsson felt comfortable confiding in a friend of 15 years' standing. In 1862, when Ericsson's *Monitor* fame had just been telegraphed around the world, Adlersparre, then a high official of the Swedish Ministry of Naval Defense, contacted him. By the greatest good luck the official was visiting New York, and wished to call upon his fellow countryman to express his admiration. Clearly Ericsson battened on the admiration. But Ericsson also made ample use of Adlersparre during the years that followed, both as an ear to the ground for Swedish military developments and as a conduit for Ericsson's many technical proposals for Swedish coastal defense, in which the inventor retained a deep interest.

Writing again in June, 1876, Ericsson thanked his admirer for certain clippings, doubtless about Swedish defense matters. "But why did you not send the whole paper?" he complained. "Allow me now to urge you henceforth to send the entire newspaper. In hardly a single instance do I know the date of the many clippings you have, in your kindness, sent me. Something else that always interests me is, in which corner of the paper the editor has placed the subject.

"Concerning the Philadelphia exhibition, you will soon find that my absence from it will prove to be of the greatest benefit to me."[2]

At the beginning of August, he expressed the hope that "a Centennial brochure" has arrived in Adlersparre's hands intact.[3]

"The account promised therein is going to constitute a mighty rejoinder, to be distributed gratis, with the title *A Gap in the Centennial Exhibition filled by John Ericsson.* I thank God for this fortunate opportunity to place my more important accomplishments *in this country* before the world and generations to come. The book is going to be translated into Swedish at once. Professor Ångström and Director Elworth have accepted the assignment of arranging for it." We know by Ericsson's note to Hjalmar, enclosing his letter of introduction, that at their brief first meeting he had shown his son a 'brochure,' and may have given him a copy. However, this preliminary publication was as slim as it sounds and from it Hjalmar could not have known what he was getting into.

Ericsson had a small favor to ask of Adlersparre, and dropped a hint: "A pity that I have antagonized Professor Edlund seeing as he is now among those people I would especially wish to entrust with its translation."[4] Professor Erik Edlund, a physicist, was a member of the Royal Swedish Academy of Sciences.

By late September, Ericsson thanks Adlersparre for letters in July and August, along with issues of the Stockholm evening newspaper *Aftonbladet* and the minutes of a parliamentary session in which defense was discussed. But he was also grateful for "your offer to persuade Professor Edlund to take part in the translation of my book, which now, thank God, is completed and in press."

"With the illustrations, it contains 720 pages quarto. The weight of it is going to exceed 9 pounds because the pages, meant to withstand centuries of turning and leafing through, consist of unusually sturdy paper. Despite the extent of this book, a significant part of my works in America are only mentioned. Truly I have never before realized the scope of my own efforts. It should be self-evident that only those projects which have been *carried out on American soil* can be mentioned in a book whose title is and must be *A Gap in the Centennial Exhibition filled by John Ericsson.* Concerning the Centennial brochure, may I say that it was written in great haste for the exhibition's prize-judges and for the correspondents of the most notable foreign newspapers, to counteract the American outrage of erasing my name from the occasion. Only 200 copies have been printed. Not a single copy have I given to any American newspaper or individual, with the exception of a few close friends."

The book is going to be distributed free, Ericsson told Adlersparre, to all the larger libraries and institutions of higher learning, but to rather few individual persons. "I assume that 500 copies ought to be enough for Sweden and [Norway] – More on this subject when the book is transmitted."[5]

On New Year's Eve Ericsson wrote Adlersparre again. As he had so often before, he opened on a technical subject that had come to consume much of his time – the development of a counterweapon for the ironclad – an explosives-laden waterborne projectile and the vessel to deliver it.

"Swedish coastal defense ... must consist of small vessels lying low in the water, equipped with mobile torpedoes which can be launched near the vessels' bottoms. ...

"I am very pleased to tell you that I have succeeded in the highest degree in simplifying my torpedo and minimizing its cost. ... This wonderful wooden fish is now almost ready, and is going to be tested by the Navy Department early next spring. ...

"Now to other subjects ... your question, 'Has the Creator's intention to make all living beings happy failed so totally as seems the case on earth?' Such a question could ... justifiably be asked of one who is now a witness to the conditions among New York's foreign inhabitants. Over 50,000 men, women and children are presently without any other bread than the crumbs distributed by charity, and a large number of these unfortunates even lack any shelter. Note: most of the hungry are willing to work, and beg for employment! Truly this is a frightful struggle. Happily, your question 'Does the struggle continue on the other side of the grave' can be answered with an emphatic negative. ...

"The printing of the mighty book is being driven at maximum speed, but since I have calculated that over 700 copies are required for distribution, with consequently 50,000 illustrations, the work is not going to reach the bookbinder's hands before the end of February. That this work will excel everything that has been published here or elsewhere is now completely assured.

"It is satisfying in the highest degree that Professor Edlund has promised to recommend a qualified translator and that he is willing to examine and correct the work. ..."[6]

In January, 1877, John Ericsson wrote to his son, who had now been back in Sweden about four months. The letter is in the fine clear hand of his secretary Samuel W. Taylor, though the language is Swedish.

"My dear Hjalmar:

"In accordance with our last conversation regarding my book, I have been expecting a letter from you saying that you have succeeded in finding people engaged in science who are willing to undertake its translation. Probably you have been too busy with your [travel] report to keep your promise in this matter. Meanwhile I have exchanged letters with Commodore Adlersparre. He writes that Professor Edlund is prepared, as concerns the scientific portion of the book, not only to recommend a translator conversant with the subject but, page by page and line by line, to check and correct the completed translation.

"As for the practical or mechanical portion of the book, Professor Ångström promised me, when he visited just before leaving for home, that he would devote his time to its translation. The book is now printed, but because the illustrations are going to require nearly six weeks, it cannot be sent to Sweden before the end of March.

"Please visit Commodore Adlersparre and Professor Ångström and settle the matter with them. As regards the cost, I am willing to pay any sum whatever to make the translation *perfect*. I told Professor Ångström that I wanted the translation sent to me before it was printed. Thinking it over, I find that altogether unnecessary since I would not dare to make a single change. So now my wish is for the book to be printed as soon as the translation is completed. Probably 200 copies in Swedish will be sufficient, for libraries and the institutions of higher learning. In English, 700 copies are being printed for distribution in both hemispheres. ...

"I will not look for your answer until you and Commodore Adlersparre and Professor Ångström have decided everything in detail.

"Present my friendly greeting to your beloved Sophie.

"With warm affection, J. Ericsson"

A postscript appears in Ericsson's own hand, mentioning that he is "intensely" occupied with his torpedo development project.[7]

On the 2nd of March Ericsson acknowledged a letter from Hjalmar in February with the comment "the contents are satisfactory so far." He offered some help:

"To aid in the translation I am going to send you a copy of my book divided up into 45 separate books, each containing a single chapter with its illustrations. Dr. Forssman knows English sufficiently to be able to convey the spirit of what I have written.

"Remember to decide Professor Edlund's pay for correcting the work's scientific portion, somewhat more than half of the whole book. As for the practical portion, its translation demands considerably more than the ability to describe machines. Therefore I advise you – just between us – to have Professor Ångström assisted by some experienced writer. ...

"As soon as it arrived I read the part of your [travel] report that was reprinted in *Jernbanebladet* [*Railroad Journal*]. This seemed to me somewhat incomplete, but in accordance with your letter I suppose that the supplement contains the full details."[8]

Two weeks later, Adlersparre was sent a short Swedish note in Ericsson's own hand ("my secretary is seriously ill") telling his friend that he has changed the book title, "A Gap in the Centennial Exhibition Filled by John Ericsson," about which Adlersparre had expressed misgivings. His book would now be called "Contributions to the Centennial Exhibition." Ericsson pointed out that this title meant none of his inventions after May 1876, the opening of the fair, would be included. He thought this explanation necessary "so that you will not promise your friends information that is not going to be given."[9]

In March Ericsson forwarded to Hjalmar the promised 45 printed sections of *Contributions to the Centennial Exhibition*. But all parts are not the same, he was careful to point out.

"... The part whose contents Professor Edlund should examine [is] the first 22 chapters as well as the last, i.e., 45th chapter. Before you turn these 23 chapters over to him, I wish him, Commodore Adlersparre and Professor Ångstrom to see the complete set, to gain knowledge of the extent of the work and the perfection of the illustrations. Such a work has never before been published in any country.

"Since the English edition is immediately going to be distributed in Europe and America, you understand that the Swedish translation can take all the time it requires. Nevertheless, not a single day should be *wasted*, for I wish my countrymen who are growing up to be able, as soon as possible, to put to use what I have accomplished in the field of physics – a labor that has cost me more than 40 years of effort. ...

"I am curious to know what the gentlemen in question say when they have examined the illustrations in the sections of the book."[10]

It was late in April before Ericsson wrote again to his son, this time enclosing a draft for 5,000 francs, "which you can immediately exchange for Swedish crowns and so be prepared to pay for the translation of the book, as the work progresses.

"By all means make use of Dr. Löfmann, since he is always available. ...

"Kindly send me a copy of the book's first chapter when it has been translated, in a clear and readable hand, so that I will have the chance to judge the translator's qualifications.

"By express today I am sending you a copy of the splendid book."[11]

This copy of Ericsson's English-language book had arrived in Sweden by May 26, when Hjalmar sent it over to Commodore

Adlersparre "for your kind examination. I should like to know when it may be picked up again, for further circulation."[12]

Through the years, in New York, Ericsson had hired Swedish translators. One of them wrote about the experience of working with the inventor. Dr. William Henschen, a Swedish editor on a visit, was hired in 1874 to translate a paper of Ericsson's that may later have become one of the chapters of *Contributions*.

"During his long stay in England and in America," Henschen wrote, "English had become his natural language, and at first we used that. But then he interrupted himself with the remark that we should be speaking Swedish, and in his mother tongue, too, he spoke quite well, even though writing went better for him in English than in Swedish. I had the opportunity to observe the extreme precision in details that always distinguished him when, on going through a printer's proof shown to him, he remarked that I quite often used [a certain Swedish word] instead of [another], but this was said in a tactful way without the least suggestion that he understood Swedish better than the translator. About style and format and such he was also very precise, for he wanted everything perfect that was going to be published under his name... Personally he gave an impression of dignity and independence and yet of friendliness."[13]

A somewhat different spirit was evidenced in Ericsson's letter to Hjalmar late in June, 1877. "I am awaiting with curiosity," he says, "the evidence of the translators' abilities." In the meantime, he expresses enthusiasm for the first volume of a scientific work newly published by a Swedish professor; he wishes his son to contact its author "immediately," buy 6 copies, and inquire "when the second volume of his extraordinary work will be published."

"Of course," Ericsson added in a postscript, "you will send me the second volume of this work as soon as it is published."[14] He himself lost no time: during July the paper, illustrations and portraits (the frontispiece engraving of Ericsson) for the Swedish edition of *Contributions* would be shipped to Hjalmar.

On July 3 a review of Ericsson's English-language *Contributions* volume written in Swedish by Commodore Axel Adlersparre appeared in a Stockholm daily newspaper:

Literature

Contributions to the Centennial Exhibition in Philadelphia 1876.
By John Ericsson.

"We have already stated that Captain John Ericsson in New York has published a larger work, *Contributions to the Centennial Exhibition,* in which he reviews the most important of his studies and inventions in the fields of physics, mechanics and weapon science, and also that he has given costly bound copies of this to our university and the Royal Library. This valuable effort, however, covers only what the celebrated scientist has accomplished during his sojourn in America, or after 1839. The reason for this is, as the title suggests, that his chief purpose has been to fill a gap in the Philadelphia exhibition's presentation of the history of scientific research in the United States. ...

"The newly published, typographically especially elegant book, in large quarto format, is divided into 45 chapters. Each chapter, accompanied by one or more illustrations, totaling 67 plates, describes one invention or one scientific finding. Thus, the first 22 chapters contain, besides the description of several physical instruments that he has constructed, his researches and findings concerning the *transmission of radiant heat; radiation at different temperatures; the intensity of solar radiation; the mechanical power of solar radiation, etc.* The contents of these chapters, though of interest to scientists, are not suitable for detailed description in a general-circulation periodical.

"In the next 10 chapters Ericsson describes the following list of his inventions and constructions. *Distance instrument*, constructed for the American navy. This instrument is used to measure the distance to the enemy's ship so as to determine the correct elevation for the cannons. *Steam fire engine*, winner of a prize competition held by the Mechanics' Institute of New York. *Steamship Princeton*, the first propeller-driven warship, which became the prototype for new construction of fighting ships. *Twelve-inch wrought-iron gun and carriage*. These cannons were the armament of the frigate *Princeton*. ... The forging in those days, however, was not up to standard and one of these cannons exploded aboard the *Princeton*. *Submerged propeller vessels for commercial purposes.* According to an accompanying table...the American merchant fleet as early as 1843 included no less than 42 of these vessels. *Iron-clad steam battery with revolving cupola,* equipped with tubes through which torpedoes can be fired by steam. ... *Surface condenser*, patented in 1849. *Caloric engine* built for the hot air driven vessel *Ericsson*. ... *Caloric engine for domestic purposes.* Many thousands of these machines have been in use. ... *The Monitor system*, an invention well known in our country. In this chapter, moreover, an excerpt is quoted from the report of a commander of an American monitor, in which he tells how with his vessel he went through waves 23 or more feet high in a storm off the American coast. Here, to the honor of science, the reader should be reminded how a mechanical invention and a newly built vessel, in the form of the first little *Monitor*, at Hampton Roads on the 8th of March 1862 defeated a many times larger opponent, the ironclad frigate

Merrimack, a victory which is said to have been a decisive turning point in the American Civil War, with the result that the United States were saved from dissolution and four million negroes were freed from slavery.

"The 33rd chapter represents a protest against the kind of monitor turret that, without consulting Ericsson, was shown at the Philadelphia exhibition. The chapter that follows concerns the *Monitor* engine. The next chapter describes the monitor *Dictator*, the largest monitor ever built. ...

"The 42nd chapter describes *a new attack weapon*, i.e., that with small charges out of 15-inch cannons torpedoes are fired that, having reached the surface of the water, take an underwater course toward an enemy warship. The following chapter describes the *torpedo boat* with whose completion our celebrated countryman has been occupied in recent years. Their propulsion is accomplished with compressed air... Chapter 44 concerns the *transmission of mechanical power through compressed air.*

"Finally, the 45th and last chapter describes the *solar engine.* By means of solar rays this machine produces motive power, either by creating steam or by heating atmospheric air. ...

"We conclude here this short review of John Ericsson's account of the work he has carried out since he came to America. It can be said with confidence that never before has any scientist or engineer developed so versatile an enterprise as our distinguished countryman, and it would be difficult to name anyone whose inventions have won greater success or brought with them greater consequences. Should anyone think this an overstatement, let us remind them only of what trade and seafaring have gained through the discovery of the propeller ship, as well as the political and social outcomes of the first monitor's appearance. And who knows what his equally brilliant and daring invention, the solar machine, is going to mean for industry and the individual household? That he has not always achieved the goals he sought, that is part of the human condition; only someone who never attempts anything never makes a mistake. Should the praises he has garnered ever have been exaggerated, neither have those bitterly envious of him been silent, and since through his military inventions he has forced systemic changes, he has also antagonized the traditionalists. However, nothing is more certain than that once his still untiring brain has ceased to labor, and he himself departed to that land from which none ever return, then at last he will be, like many another great man, rightly admired and recognized."[15]

Everything points to this effort having been volunteered by Adlersparre in a spirit of good will, if not outright adulation. Even the hackneyed peroration seems to have been meant to flatter John Ericsson.

Fifteen years before, when the walls of New York rang with excited praises of Ericsson's new *Monitor*, Axel Adlersparre had called on his fellow countryman in New York. Among the credentials he presented to the new American hero were the six years he had once, as a young man, spent as an ordinary able seaman in the American Navy. And by 1862 Ericsson's visitor had advanced to a close subordinate of the minister of naval defense in Stockholm. Adlersparre's thorough grounding in all naval matters must have been impressive to Ericsson, who in matters maritime was largely self-taught. The sea lay a long way from the little mining community of Långbanshyttan. Axel Adlersparre was a descendent of a famous Swedish family, besides. The visitor had no difficulty persuading Ericsson to let Sweden send a skilled draftsman to make copies of his *U.S.S. Monitor* drawings, though no one in the U.S. Navy was consulted, and though the Navy turned down Denmark's request for the same drawings.

There was no doubt the Swede and the Swedish-American became useful to one another. Adlersparre basked in the reflected glory of Ericsson's sudden worldwide fame, for 15 years conveying to the Swedish military establishment Ericsson's many proposals of new weapon inventions and tactics. He also served up the latest news about Sweden's evolving defense posture to Ericsson's eager ear. Whenever Ericsson needed a soothing application of sincere admiration he would write to Adlersparre with confidence. Adlersparre, after all, had written that he intended to become Ericsson's biographer (though he never did anything about it).

What, then, could have prepared the Swede for the impact of this terse, tense English-language response to the clipping of his book review that he had sent his Swedish-American idol?

"New York, August 3, 1877
Dear Commodore:

"Even though your letter and the ...newspaper article of July 3 have now been in my hands for 11 days, I am still not calm enough to write you on this subject. That your mutilated presentation of the contents of my book, your defective description of said book, and especially your attack in the last sentence of the article would anger me extremely should be self-evident. This book cost over $15,000 dollars and the solar power and radiant heat calculations, etc., you have excluded cost me 10 years of labor and $100,000 of investment.

"My next letter is going to contain certain questions I want you to answer. But until I have cooled off somewhat from this rude shock I dare not, as I said, put those questions.

"With warm greetings to Mrs. Adlersparre, I remain your devoted servant, J. Ericsson."[16]

NOTES

1. Ericsson, John to Axel Adlersparre, Apr. 25, 1876. The International Exhibition's official opening in Philadelphia was scheduled for May 10, just two weeks later. The legendary *Monitor* now seems destined, like the *Flying Dutchman*, to sail on forever, but problems with the ironclad stirred controversy among naval professionals even before the Civil War was over. David A. Mindell, 2000, 118-122, summarizes and clarifies this long controversy, and Ericsson's tenacious misapprehension of the criticisms. Ericsson probably proposed to the 'jury' that the 1876 Centennial Exhibition feature a dramatic presentation of the *Monitor*'s 'victory' that would lay all these ghosts to rest, but the Navy Department was unwilling to feature anything so controversial. Their only concession to *Monitor*'s fame was an immobile wooden replica of the famous gun turret that Ericsson took as a personal affront.
2. Ericsson to Adlersparre, Jun. 23, 1876.
3. Ericsson, John, 1876a.
4. Ericsson to Adlersparre, Aug. 4, 1876.
5. Ericsson to Adlersparre, Sept. 22, 1876. See Ericsson, John, 1876b.
6. Ericsson to Adlersparre, Dec. 31, 1876.
7. Ericsson to Hjalmar Elworth, Jan. 19, 1877.
8. Ericsson to Elworth, Mar. 2, 1877.
9. Ericsson to Adlersparre, May 26, 1877.
10. Ericsson to Elworth, Mar. 23, 1877.
11. Ericsson to Elworth, Apr. 27, 1877.
12. Elworth to Adlersparre, May 26, 1877.
13. Skarstedt, Ernst T., 1917, 232-3.
14. Ericsson to Elworth, June 22, 1877.
15. *Svenska Dagbladet*, July 3, 1877.
16. Ericsson to Adlersparre, Aug. 3, 1877.

CHAPTER 14

Not until almost two months had passed did John Ericsson cool off enough to write Adlersparre a crisply detailed 9-page indictment of his failings. He wrote all nine pages in English, in long horizontal strokes and minimal vertical spikes, and then had them copied into the crisp upright professional hand of his secretary S.W. Taylor. Taylor, after all, had learned his copyist skills in a court of law, and it was something very much like a court that Ericsson meant to convene:[1]

"My dear Commodore,

I beg to acknowledge the receipt of your favor of 22d August. However, before expressing my views regarding your remarkable notice of 'Contributions to the Centennial Exhibition' I am compelled, in order to establish my rights to speak, to remind you in the most friendly spirit that the publication of the contents of a book presented as a token of friendship, without consulting its author, involves a serious breach of confidence. That the work was printed only for private circulation and not intended to be sold, you have always known; hence my amazement on finding a notice of it under the heading of 'literature.'

"Had you been competent to write a proper account of my contributions to American progress during the last third of the first century of the Republic, as set forth in the book, your publishing the same without my consent might be attributed to friendly impatience to do justice; but you exclude two thirds of my labor, and you do not even permit the reader to contemplate the meager part put before him without distracting his attention by adverting to my mistakes and my failures in other matters; and, worse than all, you assert that I have been the recipient of exaggerated praise. A person contending that these remarks are not unfriendly and injurious, besides being highly inappropriate on the occasion, is simply insincere. What more could a bitter enemy do than calling the reader's attention to the author's failures, in order to prevent his receiving full credit for the labors recorded? Be well assured my dear Commodore that my opponents have chuckled over the concluding part of your review ...

"I will now proceed to present my 'case,' confident that when submitted to the proper tribunal, it will be found that there is *more* than 'one man on this earth' who thinks that you have subjected me to an unmerited infliction by laying before the Scandinavian world a defective, not to say misleading, account of the contents of the book which records some of my contributions to human progress.

The book itself.

"In your letter to *me* you say: '*maken till bok finnes icke.*'[2] In addressing the Swedish public you say: typographically, the book is '*särdeles prydlig.*'[3] You could not have selected a worse phrase, nor one that more inadequately tells what the work is. Competent persons both in America and Europe say, that such a work has never been published in connection with mechanics and physical science. The illustrations are pronounced as unequaled for accuracy and perfection. Having incurred such great expense, devoted so much time, and taken such great pride in the matter, I felt deeply mortified that you did not see fit to tell my countrymen what sort of a book I had presented to the world. Had you devoted half a dozen lines for this purpose, and *omitted* some fifty objectionable lines at the close of your review, you would have added to the many obligations under which you have placed me in times gone by.

"The American Philosophical Society, which is the highest scientific institution in the United States, on receiving my Contributions to the Centennial Exhibition, directed its secretary to say: 'your very superb book will be one of the chief historical monuments and ornaments in its library.' In my native land the work is noticed merely as a literary production which is typographically '*särdeles prydlig.*'

The contents of the Book

"Your reference to the contents of the first 22 chapters (which includes nearly two thirds of my work) conveys the erroneous idea that it has been written for Scientists only.

I regret beyond expression your statement that the said part of my book '*ehuru af intresse för vetenskapsmännen*'[4] is not sufficiently practical to warrant its insertion in the columns of a public journal. The truth is, that my book interests all, and may be read by every educated person. Indeed it interests society at large. You have consequently wholly misconstrued the character of my book and unintentionally misrepresented its author, who has *never* written for merely scientific readers. ...

Failure to reach the object sought -

Receiving exaggerate [*sic*] praise.

"Your object in referring to the above points in an article purporting to inform the Swedes of the nature of the contributions of their countryman to the great American centennial celebration, is simply inexplicable. On submitting the matter to a man of great judgment and cool head, a few days ago, he said to me: 'The reference to your failures is unquestionably injurious to your professional standing in the eyes of most people, and it tends to lessen the glory which your book confers.' He further suggested, that the reviewer possibly intended to administer a gentle rebuke to the author's pride, or to shift responsibilities from the shoulders of others unto his. 'If that be not so,' he added emphatically, 'then your friend has committed an astounding blunder in adverting to your failures while describing your wonderful contributions to American progress. ...'

Concerning the last sentence of the review

"Your concluding remark places me in a false position before my countrymen, as it conveys the impression that, like others that have gone before me, I am neglected. So far from that being the case, I enjoy while I live, more than a full share of approbation. The engineering fraternities of England and America, representing as they do 80,000,000 of my fellow men, admit by common consent, that I have no peer. Accordingly, as your humble servant receives full credit for what he has done, it would have been true had you, in concluding your review, conveyed the idea that unlike others that have gone before him, he is neither neglected nor poor, but appreciated and rich.

"Should you consider the foregoing statement of my case, needlessly long, I beg of you to recollect, that in your letter of 22d August you accused me of having subjected you to unjust reproaches (*orättvisa förebråelser*). I shall deem no letter too long – no trouble too great – to convince you that my 'reproaches' were founded on truth and justice. That your *intentions* were not unfriendly, permit me to remark, does not alter facts, nor mitigate the damage sustained. ...

"With kind regards to Madame, I am
My Dear Commodore
Yours very truly,
J. Ericsson"[5]

Was the gravest of Adlersparre's offenses that he excluded the first 22 chapters from his review of the contents, saying they were only intended for 'Scientists'? By doing so, he may have deflected Ericsson's arrow from its target, which he had said was the education of the Swedish young.

Ericsson had written Hjalmar in March that he wanted the book translated and published in Swedish because "I wish those of my countrymen who are growing up to be able, as soon as possible, to put to use what I have accomplished in the field of physics – a labor that has cost me more than 40 years of effort..."[6]

There was a longstanding Swedish tradition of seeking education abroad, to bring new technical knowledge home to Sweden, as Christopher Polhem had done. As a young man in 1794-6 Polhem had traveled to Germany, Holland, Belgium, France, Switzerland, Denmark and England, and then brought home a trove of technical observations that he spent the rest of his life applying to Swedish industrial development. This may be why Ericsson was so unwilling to concede that the portion of *Contributions* he considered to be of the greatest importance was less than accessible to every educated reader.

In mid-November, a letter from Commodore Adlersparre reached the inventor, in which the parliamentarian defended his published review of *Contributions*. Ericsson's response was in English, crisply copied by his scribe:

"...Although I am somewhat pressed for time today, there is an expression in your letter which demands instant attention - you say: '*Och underligt låter det* nu*, att England och Americas ingeniörer enhälligt erkänna att Herr Kaptain står öfver dem alla* '[7] Your emphasizing the word '*nu*' proves that you are wholly ignorant on the subject. A few years ago England (not America) possessed mechanical men who might, with some show of reason, have been put forth as my equals; but they are all dead, hence now no mechanical man can be named, in either country, who has accomplished one half, nor even one fourth, of what I have effected. ... Moreover, the publication of my book has revealed the fact to my mechanical bretheren [*sic*], that my labours take in the whole range of mechanical philosophy, and that I have solved numerous important problems which have perplexed the greatest men of science of this and former times. ..."[8]

More such salvoes were fired eastward across the Atlantic Ocean on June 21, July 9 and July 31. When the last of these arrived in Stockholm, Adlersparre happened to have gone out of town, leaving it to his wife Sophie to open his mail.

Sophie Leijonhuvud and Axel Adlersparre had been married in 1869 (receiving glowing congratulations and costly gifts from Axel's friend John Ericsson). Sophie was widely known as the Swedish translator of Charles Dickens' novels; she was also an organizer of women's mutual aid organizations as well as the founder and editor of one of the earliest Swedish feminist magazines.

So when Sophie Leijonhuvud Adlersparre opened the latest broadside from ironclad John Ericsson and decided it was time to take up her husband's defense, it was no popgun rejoinder she fired back.[9]

Nearly three months passed before Ericsson replied, as usual addressing Axel Adlersparre. He enclosed Sophie's letter and asked her husband to return it to her, saying that he had only read the first of its 6 pages, "as that page convinces me that the lady does not comprehend the subject she undertakes to discuss."[10]

By now, Adlersparre might have been feeling battle fatigue or very possibly the onset of ill health. He wrote Ericsson to protest his continuing friendship for the inventor, and to apologize for their misunderstanding even if he does "not think infallibility is possible for anyone but God."[11]

Despite the fury of his attacks, Ericsson was not one to hold a grudge, so he quickly replied in a conciliatory vein, asking about the reception in the Swedish parliament of his latest weapons proposal.[12]

When he received Adlersparre's answer, he sent a telegram: ACCEPT MY THANKS FOR YOUR CLEAR AND SATISFACTORY REPLY MONDAY.[13]

So John Ericsson had his Swedish correspondent back, and kept his sometime admirer busy on some more questions for a couple of months. But Ericsson's letter of May 23, 1879 was "opened and read by L. Lund [a physician?] but never mentioned to Axel Adlersparre, who was then confined to his bed."[14] On the 16th of June, 1879, Adlersparre died.

NOTES

1. Ericsson's experience of courts of law was, unfortunately, extensive. Two Swedish encyclopedias state that he was once imprisoned for debt even in his home country, though nothing confirming this has been found. In England, he and his first partner, Braithwaite, were parties to a suit over patent rights long before Ericsson's own astonishing debt sent him into debtor's prison on two different occasions, in 1832 and 1835. In America, after the accident on the warship *U.S.S. Princeton*, Ericsson brought suit to recover his expenses, a suit that continued, without success, for decades.
2. "The book has no equal"
3. "Especially elegant"
4. "Though of interest to scientists"
5. Ericsson, John to Axel Adlersparre, Sept. 27, 1877. Ericsson's brief letter of August 3 must have been passed to Erik Edlund of the Academy. Among Adlersparre's papers at Kungliga Biblioteket. Stockholm, Sweden, is a 2-page note from Edlund dated September 18, 1877, saying that he thought Ericsson's reactions "astonishing and unwarranted" and supported Adlersparre wholly.
6. Ericsson to Hjalmar Elworth, Mar. 23, 1877.
7. "And how extraordinary to hear *now* that the engineers of England and America admit by common consent that you have no peer."
8. Ericsson to Adlersparre Nov. 16, 1877.
9. Adlersparre, Sophie L. to Ericsson, Aug. 20, 1878.
10. Ericsson to Adlersparre, Nov. 22, 1878.
11. Adlersparre to Ericsson, Dec. 9, 1878.
12. Ericsson to Adlersparre, Jan. 2, 1879.
13. Ericsson to Adlersparre, N.Y. telegram No. 3689, Feb. 24, 1879.
14. Annotation, very likely by Sophie A., on the Ericsson original letter of May 23, 1879, now in Kungliga Biblioteket. In October of 1881, Sophie wrote to

Ericsson to ask for the return of Axel's letters. His reply, in January, 1882, refused on the grounds that they would only fuel partisan controversy and besides, the issues taken up in them have all been 'canceled' by the progress of science and of his own work.

CHAPTER 15

In the meantime, John Ericsson's project of giving his American "contributions" their own stately residence in the Swedish language advanced steadily, though Hjalmar Elworth's reports on the work of the translators, editor and printer he was supervising were sometimes long in coming. By the end of August 1877 Ericsson complained he had not heard from Hjalmar for more than two months. But the father seems to be addressing a scapegrace subordinate, rather than an obliging son who has other responsibilities to discharge.

"My dear Hjalmar:

Allow me to urge you to acknowledge receipt of my letters, in accordance with the first rule of business life. Your silence has given me more anxiety than I can describe. To send an answer only after an assignment *has been carried out* does not work, seeing as that often takes many months. I have not heard from you since the 25th of June! That you had not visited the translators before you wrote that letter was totally wrong, and that you did not, immediately on your return from your travels, check on what they had done and write me about it surprises me.

"The illustrations for the Swedish book are printed, and packed together with the portraits.[1] The paper, too, is ready and packed. All of this (6 large boxes) will be sent to Stockholm next week. A copy of the book (as a sample for the bookbinder and printer), together with 'electrotypes' of the text, are also going to be sent. Of course you will pay the customs fees out of the money I sent you.

"On the 18th of May I sent my book to Baron John Ericson,[2] the Academy of Military Sciences, the Scientific Society in Uppsala, and the Engineers' Association. Not a single answer yet! Be so kind, therefore, as to ask among your acquaintance whether the book has arrived. ...

My letter to you of June 22 is still unanswered! With warm affection,

J. Ericsson"

Though the Swedish letter is in the clear professional hand of S.W. Taylor, the postscript is in Ericsson's own hand. Oddly, it has the character of a cryptic apology: "P.S. Do not expect too much of my secretary, who copies things in the Chinese way, since he does not understand a word of Swedish."[3]

Two weeks later, Ericsson writes again to Hjalmar with major changes in plan: "My original intention not to take any role in the translation has given way since I read Dr. Forssman's Chapter 1. I now intend to correct and rewrite each chapter and transmit a copy to you to be delivered to the printer, once Professor Edlund has read and approved it. By all means let Dr. Löfman check every chapter and make whatever changes seem necessary to him. However, in most cases I am not going to accept all such changes. Please drive this matter forward as fast as possible. I hope that we can be ready for the bookbinder within one year; but if you do not send me a chapter a week this absolutely cannot be done. Pay whatever the worthy translators and others ask, without involving me in the decision. By no means forget Professor Edlund's compensation. Write [the translations] out in a fair hand on single sheets, on one side of the paper only, using the best kind of paper. If possible, write even clearer than the first chapter, so that my Chinese secretary will be able to handle it. ... Dr. Löfman must enter his alterations with utmost clarity.

"Please arrange for the printing to begin as soon as the paper arrives. A written contract with the book printer will probably be necessary. That the typefaces must be of the same size as in the English original I need not say. Before you print the Swedish captions for the illustrations, I wish to see the translations.

"Convey my thanks to Dr. Forssman ... The translation demonstrates that Dr. Forssman is entirely at home both in the subject and in the English language. Please tell everyone that my secretary does not understand a word of Swedish, a matter that greatly magnifies my difficulties and entitles me to their indulgence. Further, you must let everyone know that all the punctuation marks are copied from Dr. Forssman's original, and that I am not going to concern myself with them, seeing as I do not know what Swedish punctuation rules require. ...

"Illustrations, portraits and paper for 200 copies in 6 boxes (valued at $950 dollars) were shipped to Hull yesterday on the *Otranto* – a bill of lading is enclosed. The illustrations are in Box No. 1. ..."[4]

Ericsson's next letter to his son is written a mere 5 days later. Though he does not mention it to Hjalmar, he is probably in the midst of drafting the 9-page "indictment" of Adlersparre that he will mail to the commodore on September 27. That may account for the general testiness of this message to Hjalmar, even though he has now received the report he wanted:

"Your letter of August 29, along with Ångström's translation, now lie before me. Löfman's 'reworking' is unacceptable, it departs too much from the original. To the degree Löfman does not understand English and does not consult the original regularly, he should do no further reworking. It is with real anxiety I now await Ångström's next chapter, for if he cannot write any better than what you have sent me, you are going to have to rely on a more skillful pen. Make the experiment right away with Chapter I. There is no hurry, seeing as 22 chapters have to be printed before we need the translation in question.

"Answers to your questions: Since the Swedish book's introduction is going to state that English measurements and the Fahrenheit temperature scale have been used, neither metric measurements nor the centigrade scale are to be inserted any other place than the original indicates.[5] ... You already know that I consider it necessary to check the entire translation myself. Probably Dr. Löfman is not rich, so you should pay him as the work progresses. The time he sacrifices will become the best measure for deciding what to pay him. Please be generous, for I value highly his ability to check and correct. The wages of Forssman and Ångström at the rate of 10 crowns per page I pay gladly. That Dr. Forssman has already reached Chapter X surprises me. Assuming that this truly is the case, I think it necessary to send you another 5,000 francs.

"Should the Gothenburg Shipping News insert any account of the contents of my book, I urge you to inform me whether this item, against my wishes, is inserted into any other paper in the kingdom.

"Best wishes to Sophie from your warmly affectionate

J. Ericsson"[6]

"Stockholm, October 25, 1877
"My dear Father,"

Hjalmar addresses Ericsson. This is at least his seventh letter from Stockholm to his father in New York since he returned. Acknowledgments in his father's letters establish his receipt of letters from Elworth dated in February, June, August, September and now for the third time in October, 1877, though except for the text below none of these seem to be extant. Nevertheless, the son's attention to detail and his demonstration of active involvement, here, probably characterize Hjalmar's participation in the *Contributions* project right up to this point.

"The fifth chapter is enclosed. In reading through it I have made several notes in pencil, as well as placing a question mark on a passage running from page 13 to 14. This section does not seem to have any direct connection with what is expressed immediately before, making the conclusion of the passage somewhat unclear to both me and Löfman.

"I have now spoken with Haggström. He will first print a couple of pages as well as one table, and then this proof will be sent for your approval before any printing of the work begins. Each time the book is opened, at the top of each page, to the left 'Radiant Heat' appears and to the right, the chapter title. Yet since the title in Swedish may sometimes be too long to fit on one line, Haggström has asked whether it may be broken into two lines, even though such [a treatment] may not look very good. Perhaps such titles on both right and left side might be omitted, and instead just the chapter's number (e.g., First Chapter) be printed at the top of each page?

"The smaller box with the stereotypes and a copy of the book arrived here several days ago in good condition.

"Forssman was with me yesterday and said that he hopes to have finished his translation by year's end.

With filial affection,

Hj. Elworth"[7]

This formal close is repeated in every letter Elworth writes his father and will continue precisely so for the next decade. In contrast, the close of his very first letter to Ericsson, in 1872, when he was acknowledging the receipt of no more than a newspaper article, read: "Should you answer this letter and let me know something about yourself, more than anything that would please

Hjalmar."

Whatever Ericsson may or may not have written back (and no letters to Hjalmar 1872-1875 seem to be extant), his son must have gotten the message that Ericsson would have their relationship go so far, no further. The son never again signs a letter to his father 'Hjalmar.'

John Ericsson recorded on practically every letter he received not only the date of receipt but also the time it had been in transit from the sender, so we know that Hjalmar's letters from Stockholm took an average of 19 days en route. Thus Ericsson's next letter, on November 2, acknowledges the receipt of letters dated October 4 and 8, enclosing translations. They have brought him a pleasant surprise.

"... With especial satisfaction I note the unexpectedly great improvement in both translators. Rewriting is now unnecessary – to my great pleasure, since I am overwhelmed with important things to do, connected with torpedoes and other marine weapons. Besides that I now realize that my rewriting is incompatible with Professor Edlund's responsibility. However, I must have the chance to read each chapter before it is printed. Roman numerals must be used for the chapter headings just as in the original. ...

"Of course you will send me a proof of the first chapter before the printing continues – after that you may press on with the work without awaiting my reply. However, you should henceforth send a proof of each signature.

"The heading 'Radiant Heat' that is used in the first part of my book must be dropped and, as in the latter part, each page should describe the contents of the chapter – of course condensed so that only a *single* line is needed for it. I am sending back herewith Chapters II and III with rather few changes. Also I am sending, in a special envelope, all the tables in the book, for the convenience of the typesetter."

So far, so good. Praise for the translators and clear answers to Hjalmar's questions. But the letter now takes an unexpected turn:

"The books you sent, I cannot obtain from the Customs House because I cannot take the oath required, since you have not said that they belong to me. ... Truly you are entirely too sluggish at communicating. My book, for example – surely they have said something about it over there, for it or against it, which would interest me. Yet not a line from you on the subject. The homeland and everything that happens there, let me remind you, interests me ten times more than anything that happens in America. A short while ago I received from the secretary of the [Swedish] Academy of Military Sciences best wishes for my 'adopted homeland.' To this I answered, curtly: 'I recognize only one homeland. I would rather that my remains rest under a heap of stones on Swedish soil than under a marble monument in this country.'"[8]

From a mere complaint, this letter darkens into a reproach. In Ericsson's rhetoric, Hjalmar is guilty not only of omitting a Customs procedure, but also of thinking that his father has changed his patriotic loyalties. Correcting him severely, Ericsson uses his own death and interment as the unanswerable sanction.[9]

On the same day at the beginning of November, Hjalmar, too, is writing. The complaints and the questions of Ericsson's letters do not yet seem to have reached him.

"The long 6th chapter is enclosed. In this one, though, the translators diverge from each other less than in the preceding [chapters], giving me hope that a total rewriting, such as the 1st chapter required, will not be necessary.

"Among my penciled comments is a question beside Laplace's proposition, on page 21, because the sentence seems unclear to me, and also the question can arise whether this quotation, like the previous one, ought not appear in the original language."[10]

Eight days later, Hjalmar writes again.

"Enclosed is the 7th chapter, which has been in my hands for a few days, but only now have I had time to go through it.

"On page 7 of Löfman's text, as in the original, an arithmetical error occurs. That is, the amount 0.215 ought to be 0.2 according to a formula that Löfman noted in the margin. In that connection, some of the numerical amounts that follow should be changed as well.

"I will now be entirely occupied for a time with working up our cost surveys for the next two years, which will [be sent] to the Parliament."[11] His study of the costs for railroad facilities and equipment across the whole Swedish national system would have claimed his closest attention. Nevertheless, one week later, Hjalmar sends another chapter to his father:

"Chapter VIII is enclosed herewith.

"Doctor Forssman has delivered everything up to Chapter 21, but seeing as Löfman is presently unable to go through more than one [chapter] a week, the transmission cannot go any faster, for the time being.

"If Ångström's next chapter does not turn out any better than his first one, I would like to propose that Forssman receive the assignment to translate the mechanical portion of the work as well. Of course he is not trained in mechanics, but he is thoroughly at home in the terminology - and should he bump into any mechanical description he cannot handle, Löfman and I should be able to help him take care of it."[12]

Only two days later, receiving a proof Ericsson had asked for, Hjalmar writes again. Again he recommends a change in the translation. Though in charge of the translators, apparently he does not feel entrusted with this kind of decision.

"I received just now the enclosed printer's proof from Haggström, containing the first three pages of Chapter I, as well as a table from page 85, Chapter IV, printed on the 4th page to show the numerical typeface.

"As far as I can judge this proof seems to be as close to the original as it is possible to get; however, I am awaiting your approval before printing proceeds.

"Concerning the content, which is entirely the same as the excerpt sent here, I feel I should point out that [in translating the reference to] Professor Tyndall's work ...called 'Heat as a Mode of Motion' either '*drifkraft*' or '*rörelsekraft*,' both of them possible readings for the English word 'motion,' should replace the word '*rörelse*' ...[13]

Ericsson's next letter, written in his own hand, conveys a rarely mellow mood: "There are a few mistakes, but if Professor Edlund considers corrections unnecessary I am entirely content.

"Convey my thanks to Professor Edlund and tell him that his offer to work for me without compensation places me in such an embarrassing position that he really must promise me, through you, to accept at least 1,000 crowns for his trouble, at the end of the project.

"After asking advice of the learned professors, send me a proposal of the title for the Swedish translation. Truly I do not know what would suit Swedish pride and custom. As you know, it is usual to print the title and introduction last."[14]

The passage of two weeks, however, seems to have restored Ericsson's usual mood and manner. The following lecture is delivered to his son, in Samuel Taylor's official handwriting:

"My dear Hjalmar,

"I am sending you the fifth chapter herewith. The translation of the last part of page 13 is quite erroneous. The original wording follows:

"'The continuous shrinking of the sun will produce a perceptible diminution of the radiant energy transmitted to the earth in the course of a few hundred centuries, but the emissive energy for a given area of the sun will remain constant for millions of years, since the intensity developed by the falling mass will increase inversely as the square of its distance from the solar center, thus balancing the diminution of energy consequent on the reduced fall of the mass.'

"This presentation, which you and Löfman are unable to grasp, constitutes one of the most important points in this work. Consider this: should the *area* of the sun's disk diminish, the heat transmitted to the earth must also diminish although the temperature at the surface of the sun remains constant. A time will come when the sun appears no bigger than a saucer. Is it necessary for me to explain that, long before that, all the water on earth will have frozen even though the sun's surface still maintains a temperature of 4,000,000 degrees? ...

"Concerning the Swedish translation of my work, allow me to say you should not permit any changes. I wish for it to resemble the original in *all* respects. Have a look and you will see that the page headings are shorter, in many cases, than the main heading on the chapter's first page. This is usual in such English works which, when opened, always present the contents, the chapter number, and the page number. As for the proof, may I urge you to send the entire first chapter for my approval before the printing continues. This will be useful for the book's printer, who thereby can decide the price with greater confidence. I wish you to make use of the quarto format for recopying – thereby avoiding the unpleasant *double*-fold – and seeing as your last envelope was worn through on the way here, I advise you to line the inside of yours with linen, just as I do. You still have *40* chapters to send me, so these measures are not at all unnecessary. By all means write the chapter number on every page, to avoid mix-ups.

"With warm affection, J.Ericsson

P.S. [In Ericsson's own handwriting] Your letter of November 2 arrived only a few hours before this one was going to be taken to the post office."[15]

One can sympathize with the inventor's impatience with the iron interval of 19 or 20 days for mail between Sweden and the United States. But several more answers to his questions set out from Stockholm on the 25th of November:

"My dear Father,

Just back from a several days' journey on the railway lines, I have received your letter of Nov. 2 as well as the translations of Chapters II and III, and a special bundle of all the tables in the book. I am very glad to learn that you are pleased with the translators.

"I am not familiar with the procedures for customs clearance in the United States, but I thought that, if the address is marked plainly outside... then it can quite simply be handed over to the person addressed. If some special certificate from here should be needed, may I ask for the official form required, after which the certificate will be sent without delay. The books are packed in the same box in which the splendid bound copy of your book arrived, and the address is identical with the one on my letters.

"As for my sluggishness in communicating, there is not much to report since we live in the happiest and most stable country in the world, thank God, and those events that take place are discussed quite thoroughly in our newspapers, which I know you follow very closely. However, a painful condition prevails at the present time, all our industry is in a slump and our trade imbalance is quite large. No prospect for improvement in sight, either, and I am feeling some anxiety about the coming year. The unreasonably hasty pace of our railroad construction – we now have 900 miles in our national rail network and 1,800 miles in privately owned lines – may have contributed to this outcome by tying up so many millions [of our capital].

"I have not yet succeeded in finding out any opinions of your book, probably because no one has yet read it through. This is partly because the great scope of it deters one from getting started, and partly because, once one has started reading it, a good deal of time is required. For these reasons, most people may be waiting until they get the book in Swedish. I may very well hear that Professor Edlund has not yet had time to look through the book, but having taken on the editing of the translation he will, of course, go through it closely. After that I hope to be able to tell you in full his views about it.

"Chap. IX is enclosed herewith. A printing error occurs on page 179 of the original, I mean the formula $88/5^2 = 3°2$ F which should be $88/5.2^2 = 3°2$ F.

With filial affection,

Hj. Elworth.[16]

Meanwhile, on November 30, 1877, Ericsson was reacting to Hjalmar's reports of errors in the English-language *Contributions to the Centennial Exhibition*:

"My dear Hjalmar,

"I am sending you Chapters VI and VII with various changes.

"Allow me to mention that the translators need not correct my calculations. Should there be errors in the original, which now is distributed throughout the entire civilized world, I wish them to stand unchanged in the Swedish translation as well. Professor Löfman's formula was unnecessary to teach me what of course I should already know, I mean that the surface 'o' in Figure 1 in Pl. 14 is precisely 1/5 of the surrounding rectangle.

The figures I have given harmonize with my way of demonstrating my proof through the conditions recognized by every educated person. The entire work is written in such a way that the uneducated can read and understand it. Others may write in such a way as to shine with their knowledge, [but] I work to be of use. The 'calculation error' prof. L. discovered leads to an understatement of the annual shrinking of the sun's radius of exactly *one inch*. Not much, is it, when the length of the sun's radius exceeds 426,000 English miles! I am holding onto Prof. Forssman's originals, for the present, in case the revised copies should be lost. The envelope containing your letter of the 10th of this month was entirely worn through, because it was too small and the paper of poor quality.

"The trials with my new torpedo equipment have begun on the Hudson River.

"I note that you now have a great deal to do. Do not allow your kindness to me to induce you to neglect your duties as a civil servant."[17]

Hjalmar's next report, mailed to New York within the same week, summarized a very crowded schedule:

"My dear Father,

"Your letter of Nov. 9, along with the translation of Chapter IV, I received on the 27th. The next day I visited Prof. Edlund and conveyed your greetings. He thanked you and told me 'that he will be pleased, from his interest in the subject, to read through and check the translation, and that he does not regard this as a labor requiring compensation.' However, he did not really refuse to receive the amount offered on completion of the work.

"I am afraid that an obstacle has now arisen to the swift execution of the translation, because Edlund has been appointed chairman and Forssman, secretary of a committee that is to work out the regulations, etc., for the introduction of the metric system that has been decided on. Forssman has Chapter XXII ready and thinks he will need at least three months to complete the remaining chapters. But should we get them by the 1st of March, this delay would not matter so much, seeing as Löfman, during the same period, is handling Chapters XI-XXII. It would be worse if Edlund should not find the time to do the checking – I have not yet received Chapter II back from him. . ...

"To find a suitable title for the book is going to be difficult, but will no doubt prove possible once the learned gentlemen have had some time to ponder it.

"I am now on the point of departure on a longer inspection trip covering the whole national network, and do not expect to be back before the 20th or 21st of the month.

"Chapter X is not going to be ready before tomorrow, and I have asked Löfman to send it then and, further, to send in a chapter every 8th day until I return.

"Sophie asks me to convey her cordial Christmas greetings."[18]

On his return, Elworth found his father's November 30 letter, with its wish that errors in the original English volume should stand unchanged in the Swedish translation as well. That Hjalmar did not relish passing along to Forssman, Löfman and Edlund that "the translators need not correct my calculations" can be read in this reply.

"My dear Father,

"Home again yesterday from my inspection trips, I would like to thank you for your letters of the 23rd and 30th of November, enclosing Chapters V, VI and VII.

"Turning first to the presentation on page 13 of Chapter V concerning the lessening of solar heat transmitted to the earth, both Löfman and I understand that passage quite well – my question only concerned Forssman's translation, which seemed unclear to us, but which Löfman did not feel free to change. Since you yourself found reason to correct the translation, the matter is taken care of. ...

"Concerning the calculation on Pl. 14 of the surface o p l, it was not Löfman's intention at all to find fault or to show off his learning. He only mentioned to me the small difference in area, and it was only at my urging that he noted down his calculation – while I thought you wanted to have everything as correct as possible.

"When such typographical errors as may exist are detected through the checking of such calculations as may come up, we have not hitherto felt we could neglect such checking, especially since Professor Edlund, if he is to take responsibility for the scientific portions, would need to make the very same tests.

"Since the printer has cleared up the pressure of the enormous Christmas literature that gets published here, he is ready to begin the printing of the complete Chapter I, and would follow very carefully the directions he has received.

"I hope to be able to send you the next chapter in a couple of days. I shall then get some better envelopes in the quarto format, though writing paper in that format is not used in this country.

"We are not expecting a happy Christmas Eve, since Sophie is very sick with stomach pains and recovery is slow in coming."[19]

Ericsson's only December letter to his son seems a strange culmination to their year of cooperation, if not collaboration. It is written in Ericsson's own elliptical hand. Despite the success Ericsson reports, he seems tense and perhaps apprehensive.

"My dear Hjalmar,

"The 'reworking' of the introduction to Chapter VIII is unacceptable, but just now I have no time to correct it.

"I urge you to get Dr. Forssman to translate the *whole* book. His skill in describing mechanical arrangements is excellent. Tell professor Ångström bluntly that since Dr. F. is well acquainted with my style of writing I wish him to complete the entire translation.

"The outcome of my latest torpedo trials has exceeded my expectations – truly, one of the most successful projects of my entire life. I urge you to translate as quickly as possible the enclosed copy of my report to the Navy Department in Washington and get it into the *Nya Dagligt Allehanda* [newspaper]. Please see to it that the article does not get stuck into one of the newspaper's corners and that small type is avoided.

"I need not tell you that since I have now taken on the construction of a torpedo vessel faster than all of Europe's ironclads and at the same time able to defy their bombardment, both my head and my hand are going to be hard-pressed through this winter. You are aware that I use no intermediary in the preparation of original drawings.

"Give Sophie my regards and receive, both of you, warm good wishes for the new year from your cordially affectionate

J.Ericsson

P.S. Please send two copies of the newspaper containing my report. Use clear and simple language, i.e., for the translation of the report."[20]

The transit time of this last Ericsson letter of 1877 was unusually short; Elworth, across the wintry seas in Stockholm, received it in time to respond before year-end.

"My dear Father,

"Your letter of the 14th arrived yesterday. Sophie and I would like to thank you most cordially for your New Year's wishes.

"It was especially interesting to hear that the new torpedo trials had turned out so favorably. Tomorrow I am going to visit Dr. Lindström, to find a place in *Dagligt Allehanda* for the article you sent, which Löfman is already translating.

"Chapter XIII is enclosed herewith. Since there were no fabric envelopes in quarto format to be had, I have asked for our common writing paper to be cut to a suitable size for the envelopes that could be obtained.

"Among my pencil markings on Löfman's text, a question mark occurs on page 10 beside a section that none of our translators could make comprehensible, since we cannot understand the meaning of the original text. In the table on page 11 I have put a question mark on the two last columns instead of headings, because the translators did not feel able to interpret these.

"Thank God, Sophie is nearly recovered from her illness, and we join in warm wishes to you for the New Year.

"With filial affection,

Hj. Elworth"[21]

It is a truly responsive letter, promising the immediate newspaper placement of his father's torpedo report, demonstrating his efficiency with the translators, describing the best envelope alternative he can find for mailing the chapter drafts. He relays questions "the learned gentlemen" raise while himself translating and checking the translation of his father's writings. He clearly takes pride in being "on top of" the Stockholm situation that so interests his father. This new confidence and Sophie's recovery must have brightened the dark, dark Stockholm season.

NOTES

1. Copies of the frontispiece engraving of Ericsson.
2. Nils' son and heir, the same person who had sent word Hjalmar planned to visit America.
3. Ericsson, John to Hjalmar Elworth, Aug. 31, 1877.
4. Ericsson to Elworth, Sept. 14, 1877. The letter is unsigned, like the now illegible P.S. in Ericsson's own hand.
5. Professor Erik Edlund was among three members of the Royal Academy of Sciences who wrote the favorable report that led the Swedish parliament to introduce the metric system in 1876.
6. Ericsson to Elworth, Sept. 19, 1877.
7. Elworth to Ericsson, Oct. 25, 1877.
8. Ericsson to Elworth, Nov. 2, 1877.
9. Ericsson's letter to the secretary, from which he quotes this striking statement, is also extant, so we know that this self-citation is precise; yet here his statement has a rather more punitive purpose than in the first instance. Ericsson made similar statements to others.
10. Elworth to Ericsson, Nov. 2, 1877.
11. Elworth to Ericsson, Nov. 10, 1877.
12. Elworth to Ericsson, Nov. 17, 1877.
13. Elworth to Ericsson, Nov. 19, 1877.
14. Ericsson to Elworth, Nov. 9, 1877.
15. Ericsson to Elworth, Nov. 23, 1877.

16. Elworth to Ericsson, Nov. 25, 1877.
17. Ericsson to Elworth, Nov. 30, 1877.
18. Elworth to Ericsson, Dec. 2, 1877.
19. Elworth to Ericsson, Dec. 23, 1877.
20. Ericsson to Elworth, Dec. 14, 1877.
21. Elworth to Ericsson, Dec. 30, 1877.

IV

Hand to Hand

CHAPTER 16

Hjalmar Elworth was as good as his word. Six days into the new year 1878 he wrote to his father of considerable success placing the article with the newspapers. He also told him an unexpected distinction was being conferred on the author of *Contributions to the Centennial Exhibition.*

"I hope you have now received two copies of *Dagligt Allehanda* for the 2nd of this month, in which the torpedo report was inserted. These copies were mailed on the very same day published. I am enclosing a letter from Dr. Lindström in which he expresses regret that it was on the last page of the paper the report got published. We would have liked the translation to be somewhat more flowing, but since we lacked more detailed knowledge of the nature of the apparatus and the procedures used in the experiments we were not able to do so. On the following day, the report was reprinted in *Posttidning* and an excerpt of it inserted into *Dagens Nyheter*.

"I have now taken the mechanical portion of the book from Ångström and turned it over to Forssman, who is looking through it before deciding whether he dares to take on its translation. Ångström had no objection to the transfer. He has so many irons in the fire that he would probably not have found the time for translation without much delay. At the same time, he admitted he had been remiss in not having written to thank you for the book, as the Engineering Association had assigned him to do. He has been waiting upon completion of a letter inviting you to become an Honorary Member. The association has decided to elect special honorary members, no more than 10, and at their last meeting you were the first to be chosen.

"Chapter XIV is enclosed. A couple of printing errors occur in the original text, i.e., on page 242, where the equation appears as 5/15 a = 3.333 instead of 5/1.5 a = 3.333a, and on page 251, where 0.57 is printed instead of 0.057.

"Löfman proposes that a portion of pages 13 and 14 in the recopied text be eliminated, and I take the liberty to endorse this, since on pages 9 and 10 it has already been clearly stated how one calculates the values in the second column of Table A.

"Because the translator has forgotten Table B on page 16 I have drawn up a proposal for the headings in this table."[1]

Ericsson will not receive this news for the 20-odd days it will be traveling the Atlantic Ocean. His own first letter of the new year begins with sympathy:

"My dear Hjalmar,

"With indescribable sorrow I learn from your last letter, received yesterday, that your beloved Sophie is seriously ill. May your surmise that her sickness will be long- lasting not prove true."

He accepted, Ericsson wrote, a particular Swedish expression Löfman had proposed for a key concept in his description of solar dynamics. "You are entirely mistaken," he continued, "concerning Professor Edlund's 'responsibility'; he is no more responsible for my calculations than he is for the accuracy of my demonstrations. That the translation, with all the mistakes of the original (excepting typographical) is a faithful one, is all that my countrymen have a right to expect from Professor Edlund's participation. Criticism or improvement is not *translation.*

"Concerning Prof. Löfman's remark about the temperature at the sun's surface, may I say in all brevity that actinometrical investigations are independent of the changeable 'warming at the edges of the earth's atmosphere.' ... Thus the degree of warming may not be taken into the calculation.

"As for the solar pyrometer, I surmise that Prof. Löfman does not correctly realize that it can be used without regard to the position of earth in its orbit when the experiment is carried out." Ericsson then marshals mathematical proof of this.

"Since Chapter XII arrived a few days ago I now have no less than five chapters to check, but just now I cannot give them a minute because the working drawings for the new torpedo vessel and its machinery are not completed. The fact is, I am often standing at my drawing table at 11 at night, but I am so deeply interested in the subject (the most important mechanical problem I have ever solved) that I do not feel fatigued, and only put down my drawing pen because the time for my midnight walk has come.

"You know from a previous letter of mine that I do not now expect the Swedish book to come out before the end of 1879. I am mortified to think that my book, published in haste so as to punish the Centennial crowd, does not contain complete illustrations of a tenth of the mechanical projects I have carried out. But I am so wholly absorbed by the marine warfare problem that my planned expansion of the book's mechanical section must be postponed.

"Convey to Sophie in her suffering my very kindest greeting and deepest wish that she shall soon be returned to health."

"With warm affection,"[2] the letter concludes in Samuel Taylor's professional hand style, but Ericsson's signature and any possible postscript have been snipped off by some anonymous collector.

Hardly more than a week after sending his first letter of 1878 Hjalmar writes his father again.

"My dear Father,

"Herewith please find Chapter XV. In his draft of the last page, beside the passage concerning the conducting power in a thermometer bulb, Forssman has noted that this conducting power is constant. Neither Löfman nor I can see otherwise.

"The first chapter has now gone to press and I expect the first proof very soon, whereupon our agreement with the book printer will be concluded without delay.

"From Prof. Edlund I have not yet received back even the 2nd chapter. But Forssman came to me yesterday and got some money, and I asked him to remind Edlund quietly, in some appropriate way. Yet it will probably be difficult to get the chapters from Edlund as quickly as they are going to be needed for the printing.

"Since I have not heard from you for a couple of weeks, I assume that the important torpedo matter is taking up your time. It would be especially interesting to learn any details that I could mention if I should go up to the Academy of Military Sciences."

Hjalmar had not previously offered to personally pass such information along to Swedish officials; the novelty of this was not lost on Ericsson, who noted in his tiny inked index, this time inscribed right on the face of the letter rather than as usual on an outside fold: "Wants to know about Torpedo," but also noted the arresting news that came up next, "Family's misfortune."

"Werner Ericson [youngest son of the late Nils] has recently resigned from his seat in the Second Chamber [of Parliament], because of economic problems. The miserable paper pulp factory has very nearly ruined all three brothers. John may best be able to handle it, since he married a lot of money and has no children. Werner, as a bachelor, can probably get along somehow, but Carl, by contrast, is in a pitiful case with his kind lovable wife and a little daughter. He has always lived sensibly and frugally, but the factory swallowed up his entire inheritance and money he borrowed, besides. His salary as a captain [in the Army], perhaps 2,000 crowns, is not going to be enough to pay off his debt and support his family!

"Sophie, who is now completely well again, sends cordial greetings."[3]

Hjalmar writes again a week later, enclosing still another translated chapter:

"My dear Father,

"Chapter XVI is enclosed. On its first page I have placed a question mark, as both Löfman and I wanted to propose that the marked passage be deleted, since pages 7-11 give a complete account of the nature and characteristics of the barometric actinometer. Should this passage remain, it should be introduced by the pencilled-in words, as otherwise the beginning comes too abruptly.

"So far I have received from you no chapter later than VII, which arrived in mid- December."[4]

Near the end of January Ericsson writes a long letter from New York that deals out praise and blame, and then puts some questions, one of which reveals a surprising insecurity:

"My dear Hjalmar,

"Thank you for your letter of Jan. 6 with Chapter XIV and the enclosed courteous explanation from Dr. Lindström.

"*Nya Dagligt Allehanda* arrived at the usual time and I am especially pleased and satisfied with the masterful translation. It was on purpose that I made the original vague except for the results of the experiment. You do not seem to have noticed the important typographic error concerning the distance of 230 feet the torpedo raced through in 2-3/4 seconds. The newspaper says 200 feet and besides that [prints] 250/275=90 so indistinctly that it cannot be read.

"It is clear that I have not succeeded in making myself understood in a previous letter, otherwise you would not have neglected to send me *Posttidningen* and *Dagens Nyheter* for Jan. 3. I now request that you do me the favor of dispatching these papers by immediate mail. That not all the capital's newspapers inserted my report I take as a slight, for the editors are not stupid and so must know that, when just now the sea defenses of Sweden have seized the attention of the whole nation, they are absolutely unable to present their readers with anything of greater importance than my report. I expected encouragement from my fatherland, because it is for Sweden's good I now labor and expend great sums. I cannot deny that the contemptible silence of the Swedish press, on this occasion, has had an injurious effect, and to some extent impaired the boundless enthusiasm with which I have worked so long on my homeland's sea defense, convinced that if it is not strong, our struggle with Russia or Germany will become fruitless.

"Do not misunderstand me when I now express the wish that all the trouble over improving my book come to an end. Give me a faithful translation and I will become grateful. The work has gone through such stringent tests that I have reason to request that the English text be quite simply Swedished. My intention was to present a *translation* to my countrymen, not at all a corrected work. [But] that typographical errors are corrected, especially when they involve figures, will make me obliged to all of you.

"A few words about Prof. Edlund's progress on reading through the work would have been welcome. I especially hoped to learn how all of you regard the small changes I have made. Are they unacceptable – do they show a lack of practice with the language?

"What progress has the book printer made with the first chapter? The new torpedo system is still taking all my time so thoroughly that I have not been able to read through those chapters you recently sent. But now that we have postponed publication to the end of 1879 that is no longer urgent. The printer ought to be advised that we do not need him until the end of the year. However, I would like to see the *first* chapter this winter.

"You say nothing about Sophie in your latest letter, although the previous one contained the encouraging news that her health was much improved. That she is now entirely restored to health is the wish of your cordially affectionate"

In a blank space no signature appears, but in contrast to the letter text in Samuel Taylor's parade hand, the postscript below the blank is in Ericsson's own elliptical writing:

"P.S. Convey my thanks to Prof. Forssman for the quite interesting papers that, through your kindness, he sent me."[5]

Hjalmar writes again on the last day of January, sending another translated chapter, 17th of the 22 chapters of the book devoted to what Ericsson called "mechanical philosophy."

"My dear Father,

"Returning home from a trip along the western line, I received your letters of Dec. 22 and Jan. 11, both of which arrived here last Saturday.

"The torpedo article, after appearing in *Dagligt Allehanda,* was printed in *Stockholms Dagblad* on the 3rd and in *Aftonbladet* on the 4th of January.

"Forssman has now undertaken to translate the mechanical portions of the book, too, as soon as he learned that the matter is not so urgent. I met him yesterday and he promised to send me Chapter XVIII in a few days, and it is going to be fun to compare his translation with Ångström's, of which I have saved a copy.

"Chapter XVII is enclosed herewith.

"This summer it would interest me very much to be able to visit the exposition in Paris, but I am hesitating to apply for a travel grant, since I so recently received one for my trip to America.

"Sophie, who has now recovered completely, warmly thanks you for your friendly greetings."[6]

Ericsson's next letter does not even mention the book translation. The two topics Ericsson inked in his tiny bookkeeper's script on the face of Hjalmar's earlier letter, "Family's misfortune" and "Wants to know about Torpedo" have seized his whole attention, and Ericsson writes about both with unusual detail and an odd warmth.

"My dear Hjalmar,

"Thanks for your letter of Jan. 14 with the happy news that Sophie is now entirely well.

"The deplorable story of the fine gentlemen Ericson was not unexpected in the slightest degree, I only wonder that their fall did not come a great deal sooner. Carl informed me, several years ago, that *he* bought Ronneby (I think that was the name) for a sum many times greater than the little inheritance he received from his father. The sum was so great that the annual interest on it amounted to something like 10,000 crowns. That this inexperienced young man, ignorant of business matters, would not be able to earn that sum annually and meanwhile live and begin repaying the purchase price, was so obvious that his failure seemed to me only a question of time – to which your letter supplies the answer. But I did not expect to hear that he also had an interest in the unfortunate wood pulp and paper factory. So the gallant captain's situation must be frightful indeed. Swedish creditors have the right to use very severely anyone who falls into their clutches. Luckily, since his mother is rich, Carl's family, at least, will suffer no lack. John, according to your letter, has enough money through his wife, but I fear you may be mistaken. As for Werner, the troubles are likely to do him good – but may the punishment for his foolhardy way of life not become so harsh that his patience is overcome. The family's downfall, wholly because of the imprudence of its members and their idiotic behavior, is a calamity so dreadful that at the sight of it emotion overwhelms me – Thus I hasten to change the subject.

"Your wish to learn details of the nature of my torpedo experiments, so as to be able to bring up the subject at the Academy of Military Sciences, I cannot now fulfill. Enough for now that I have succeeded in hurling out a body underwater at great speed, a problem that was generally considered insoluble. Yet what remains is to construct a vessel faster than the first class armored ship, able to pursue and overtake such ships before the torpedo is hurled out. A vessel for this purpose, 130 feet long and 12 feet wide, I am now building at my own expense, to be tested this coming May. The engine is 4 feet high, standing on a base of only 8 square feet, its power exceeding 1,000 horses (actual power development). The steam pressure is 100 [pounds] per [square] inch and [its] speed only 160 strokes a minute. I have labored day and night on the working drawings and now construction in the shop is fully under way. The upper part of the vessel contains 2,000 little waterproof spaces, therefore the hull can be shot clear through without any danger of sinking. Engines, boiler and torpedo apparatus lie very deep down [in the vessel]. The rudder has no connection with the upper part of the hull, its highest point being 4 feet below the waterline, and the steering mechanism is 10 feet below that. All this you can bring up in the Academy of Military Sciences, but you will get no further details until next summer. How air is taken in, how smoke expelled, and how the captain and steersman are protected will be interesting subjects for you to think about in your idle moments."

So far the handwriting of secretary Samuel W. Taylor. But for the last line and the close, Ericsson's own hand takes over:

"The checking of the translation has to wait awhile yet. With cordial affection,
J. Ericsson"[7]

Hjalmar's reply to his father's earlier complaints is a spirited self-defense:

"My dear Father,

Yesterday I received your letter of Jan. 25 and thank you for it, sending you Chapter XVIII herewith.

"Because *Dagligt Allehanda* is published only 1/2 hour before the mail departs, and I sent the issue containing your torpedo report the same afternoon it was published, I did not notice the irritating typographical error until afterward, when it was too late to prevent the repetition of the same error in other papers.

"With today's mail I sent you separately the issues of *Posttidningen, Aftonbladet, Dagbladet* and *Dagens Nyheter* in which the torpedo report is mentioned. Of these, *Aftonbladet* has the typographical error 5.20/2.75=90 and *Dagbladet*, 250/275=90, which shows how carelessly proofs are checked at our newspapers. I have not been able to discover any mention of the report in the Gothenburg papers.

"So far, Prof. Edlund has not returned even the second chapter. Since he probably will not, before this summer, find better time to devote to the reviewing, it is especially appropriate that the publication of the work has been postponed. We have just read proofs on Chapter I, so I hope to be able to send the corrected copy next time.

"Concerning the translation of the book, there has been no intention to take the trouble to improve it, most especially since we do not have strength to do so! Our proposals have been confined to recommending the exclusion from a couple of chapters of a few passages that are found in more than one place. I have made my own what I understood to be your intention, that the book have an easy, flowing style, making it able to be placed in the hands of, and able to be understood by each and every educated, though not learned, Swede. On going through Forssman's text, when I stumbled upon sentences that he, as a theoretician, doubtless understood quite well, but that I did not find clear and obvious, I mentioned my doubts to Löfman, who, in accordance with my intention, made his text entirely lucid, where Forssman's might possibly be unclear or cryptic."[8]

Two weeks later Hjalmar took the initiative of sending an article he had noticed about the design of torpedo boats that would prove to be of great value to Ericsson. But he also mentioned Nils' widow. Her situation was far different from what his father believed.

"My dear Father,

"With today's mail I received your letter of the 8th, but I have no time now to answer it completely. However, I find that you are building a mine boat, and since a debate has recently arisen in *Dag Allehanda* concerning which construction should be chosen for 5 such boats our Government means to acquire, I assume that the enclosed article on the subject by Marine Engineer Frykholm, containing a critical review of Thornecroft's mine boat, interests you.

"From your letter I see that you imagine Countess Ericson is rich, but that is not the case because she, too, let the major part of her fortune go into the miserable woodpulp factory. Thus she is quite short of money and probably cannot help any of her sons.

"Chapter XIX is enclosed. The translators had forgotten the table showing the relative reflective power of polished metals, so I wrote that into the last page of Löfman's text and tried to Swedify the headings. ...

"The corrected Chapter I from the printer has not reached me in time, but shall be sent with my next letter."[9]

Chapter XIX is enclosed. With the Swedish translators nearing completion of the book's first half that is devoted to his father's "mechanical philosophy," Hjalmar must have felt encouraged. What remained, the "practical" chapters, made up more of a descriptive catalog of Ericsson's many inventions, surely an easier assignment both for the translators and himself. And Forssman had been Ericsson's choice to handle translating the catalog. Forssman, Löfman and himself had now begun to function as a team, even if the famous Professor Edlund was not doing his part. In Hjalmar's letter, one senses a certain momentum developing...

But his father's next letter brought them to a halt.

"New York, March 1, 1878
My dear Hjalmar,

"...Chapter XVII arrived here February 21. All the preceding chapters have reached me. I have looked through some of them, and may I tell you frankly that in Löfman's shined-up and slicked-down revision I do not recognize my own work. The forceful and convincing language that has placed me among our times' leading English writers on subjects falling within the field of mechanical philosophy, the reviser has quite simply murdered. If nothing can be done to make the translation more closely resemble the original it will never be printed. I have had Forssman's original copied over and then inserted Löfman's changes with red letters. In this way I have carefully studied the 'necessity' and content of the changes.

"The reviser's language is usually better, but the translator has the great merit of following the original more faithfully. Because of all this, I request that you not proceed with the translation of the book's practical portion, especially since I plan to enlarge and rework it.

"I enclose with the greatest pleasure 3,000 francs for your planned visit to Paris, on the condition that you take Sophie with you, so that you may both enjoy and learn from the occasion.

"With cordial affection to you both,"

But there is no signature on the letter that has survived, and a certain uncharacteristic unevenness in Samuel Taylor's handwriting of the text above suggests that this may be a draft. The postscript, also unsigned, is in Ericsson's own hand:

"P.S. Be so kind as to notify me if the translation with my comments [but] without recopying is delivered to Prof. Edlund."[10]

NOTES

1. Elworth, Hjalmar to John Ericsson, Jan. 6, 1878.
2. Ericsson to Hjalmar Elworth, Jan. 11, 1878.
3. Elworth to Ericsson Jan. 14, 1878.
4. Elworth to Ericsson, Jan. 21, 1878.
5. Ericsson to Elworth, Jan. 25, 1878.
6. Elworth to Ericsson, Jan. 31, 1878.
7. Ericsson to Elworth, Feb. 8, 1878.
8. Elworth to Ericsson, Feb. 11, 1878.
9. Elworth to Ericsson, Feb. 25, 1878.
10. Ericsson to Elworth, Mar. 1, 1878.

CHAPTER 17

"New York, March 22, 1878
"My dear Hjalmar,

"Thank you for [the clipping from] *Dagligt Allehanda* – without any date. Why not send the whole newspaper...? I now implore you, either yourself or through someone you assign, to send me all the newspapers that contain articles on naval defense.

"Your letter of January 6 did not mention that *Dagbladet* on the 3rd and *Aftonbladet* on the 4th of January published my torpedo report. You know from one of my earlier letters what mortification this negligence caused me. That Gothenburg's *Handels Tidning* for January 4 published it, you do not seem to know.

"Allow me to remind you that a courteous correspondent should not do as you do, silently pass by subjects presented to him. You do not even answer *questions*. For example, you never answered my question about the acceptability of my markings in the translation I returned to you. I have neither time nor inclination to express how I regard your penchant for silence. It amazes me that you had nothing to say when *Handels Tidning* published an excerpt from my book's scientific content, which stirred up a lot of attention. Prof. Löfman probably had something to say about that excerpt.

"What you tell me about [Nils' widow] Countess Ericson's situation is unsatisfying in the highest degree. If you know her [living] conditions, it would have been [*sic*] your duty to tell me plainly how matters stand. Where does the old woman live, and how? It annoys me that you did not touch on Carl's business dealings, a matter I brought up with you in my last letter. In a word, my dear Hjalmar, you are a feeble correspondent.

"Concerning the book, I assume that, in accordance with my wishes in my letter of March 1, you are not continuing either translation or printing, except for the first chapter."

This was different from Ericsson's March 1 request that they suspend translation of the "practical part" of the book. This made the decision more sweeping and final.

"As for Prof. Edlund, whose indifference and negligence in keeping his promises wound me deeply, may I now ask you to let him know I have found reasons to change the whole plan and so shall not be making any further claim on his precious time. I now realize that the translation of the book was a mistake, and that the distribution in my homeland of several hundred copies of the English version with a supplement would undoubtedly have been the right course.

"Consequently, may I now ask you to send back to New York, at the first opportunity, both paper and illustrations. Probably the cases are still intact, which should ease the trouble of reshipping considerably.

"Receive now my warm thanks for all the trouble you have had with the translation. You can be sure I know you worked tirelessly for the good cause.

"The development of the new torpedo system – the most difficult mechanical problem I have ever tried to solve – proceeds as I have wished in every respect.

"Convey my cordial greetings to your wife, from your warmly affectionate

J. Ericsson

"P.S. [In Ericsson's own hand:] By all means convey to Dr. Löfman my thanks for the great difficulty he has had with the translation. That he did all in his power to ensure a satisfactory outcome I understand very well. Kindly send me everything that has been translated, without any further revision. In the next mail I plan to send you instructions about the shipment of the paper."[1]

In fact, it took Ericsson until the 29th, a week later, to send instructions written out for Hjalmar by S.W. Taylor. Ericsson covered these with just 17 personally written lines, but a draft of these few lines in a much more tentative hand is also extant, its surprising number of crossings-out and interwritten changes suggesting that the author of *Contributions* had to overcome complex feelings to execute his sudden decision to end the entire project for a Swedish edition.

On March 21, thus one day before Ericsson wrote again, Hjalmar had responded to the March 1 missive, thanking for the gift of travel funds, regretting that he had not met his father's expectations but defending the accomplishments of his team. He also felt entitled to comment on his father's criticism of the translators' "improvements." From the tone, it is clear that he did not anticipate the finality of his father's decision.

"My dear Father,

"The letter of the 1st containing 3,000 francs came in yesterday's mail, and for both Sophie and myself I would like to thank you for your kindness in sending us funds for the trip to Paris. To be able to go along pleases Sophie enormously.

"That you disliked Löfman's prose makes me very sad, partly because through proposing the use of Löfman I caused an expenditure that in this case proved unnecessary, and partly because I proceeded on the assumption that you were pleased with Löfman's work.

"However, as concerns the forceful and convincing language in the English original not being found in the translation, I cannot understand this unless it depends on languages' great differences in usage. The original has many short firm sentences that could not always be retained, since in Swedish one considers it more pleasing to bring together in longer sentences everything that has immediate connection.

"Also, a good many forceful expressions occur in the criticism of experiments and findings of certain scientists, expressions which would not be thought pleasing in Swedish, where one prefers mild words if one's case is strong.

"Chapters II-VII, which I received back, have been given Edlund as they are, with your notes on them.

"The remaining chapters 20, 21, 22 and 45 of the book's physical section, Löfman has not yet had a chance to go through, and so I have had Forssman's text recopied and have asked Löfman only to pencil over it where he finds real syntax errors occurring. Forssman is engaged in translating the first chapters of the mechanical section and has been asked to cease translating, for the time being, when those chapters are ready. ...

"Concerning your statement in an earlier letter that I am too hasty in my judgments, I do not want to contest that, but when something has seemed to me unclear I have not felt I should simply keep it to myself, but have spoken up about it, to gain a clarification where it might possibly be needed.

"That you might be suffering the consequences of some controversy between myself and the translators is not at all the case. Forssman and Löfman, for example, have not yet met a single time. Only Löfman and I have spoken sometimes about the same matter coming up in different places and, to avoid being diffuse, would be better brought together in one place.

"I have just now received the enclosed final proof of Chapter I. Both the text and its setting seem to me entirely valid.

"I send herewith still another article on the torpedo question, with a defense of the use of hydraulic motors. The author's name I have not been able to learn.

"Sophie sends cordial greetings."[2]

As usual, John Ericsson chalked across the top of this letter in Swedish the date received and the time en route: "*Ankom* [arrived] April 5 = 15 *dagar* [days]." He also marked this letter in other ways that were less usual. With the same red chalk Ericsson underlined: "*hvilka ord skulle ej omtyckas i svenskan* [expressions which would not be thought pleasing in Swedish]" and, farther along, " *att samma sak förekommer på olika ställen och hade, till undvikande af vidlyftighet, kunnat vara sammanförd på ett ställe* [the same matter coming up in different places, which, to avoid being diffuse, would be better brought together in one place]" And finally, in the tiny precisely inked hand with which he often indexed particularly important letters, Hjalmar's father wrote on the last page: "'Hydraulic motor' *inneslutet* [enclosed]."

Now he had his answer. With a surprising and uncharacteristic humility, John Ericsson had asked for his translators' and his son's opinion of his own Swedish. *The "little changes" he had introduced – were they "unacceptable"? Did they mark him as someone lacking practice in the Swedish language?* And now, when his answer came back, it was worse than that, it was what he took to be a sweeping judgment on his very style and organization in expressing himself throughout the English text of his first 19 chapters — "forceful expressions" had become his natural mode, while a Swede "preferred mild words if his case was strong." His English sentences were compact thrusts, while Swedes tried to tie every related matter into longer, comprehensive sentences. In short, he took their opinion to be that, if written expression was the test, he was no longer a true Swede! "*Mild words if one's case is strong*"!! This judgment must have shocked and angered him, but he turned his face away from it resolutely, and wrote down as if this were the whole content of the letter: "Hydraulic Motor enclosed." Back to business.

But his son's next letter revealed that Ericsson's painful decision had not fully registered in Stockholm, or that Hjalmar, with his labor of many months invested in the translated version, was resisting.

"My dear Father,

"... I confess freely that I am a feeble correspondent and I am afraid that, at my age, there is no prospect of improvement. But rude, on the other hand, I want with all my heart not to be. If I have failed to answer any questions it has been because I overlooked them, and I am asking you not to blame me so heavily for this as your last letter seems to indicate. As concerns the reception given the comments you wrote on the translations you sent back to me, I did not notice any such questions in your ensuing letters. Besides, even now I am not able to answer them, since I only glanced through the returned chapters (II-VII) on receipt and immediately handed them over to Prof. Edlund, who still has them and, judging by his replies to one direct question from me and two from Forssman, has not yet had the time to go through them.

"As for the article in the Gothenburg *Handels Tidning*, neither Löfman nor I had noticed it. The [Swedish National Railway] Board subscribes to that one as well as to many others, but only now and then do we have the time to glance through them hastily. The only newspaper I subscribe to myself and read daily to keep up with what is happening is the *Dagligt Allehanda*. This is why many items in other newspapers on specialized subjects escape my notice.

"Now after searching the newspaper files I have found the issue of the *Handels Tidning* (September 22) containing the article about your important work. The article describes the book's physical section quite well, and it is a pity it has not also appeared in the larger Stockholm newspapers.

"In this article I see, too, that *Handels Tidning* has been told the book is going to be translated into Swedish, and the same has also been announced through our leading newspapers. If now, probably because of dissatisfaction with Prof. Edlund's neglect, you halt the book's publication in Swedish, this would stir up a regrettable sensation. I cannot believe that you find the translation so inept that it would not be approved by the usual critics. If you ask me, the language used is perfectly satisfactory and all the descriptions of the apparatus are clear and understandable and, besides, I would be glad to obtain the judgment of language experts. Among those who would probably be willing to undertake editing of the physical section of the translation, instead of Edlund, is my old physics teacher at Marieberg, Professor Baron Fock.

"It would be a great shame if this interesting work, with its brilliant apparatus and machines, did not become known in our homeland, for I do not expect it to become known by sitting on the shelves of a few libraries, really just as a showpiece, since not everybody is able to interpret its contents. In the hope that you will reconsider this matter, I will not re-ship the paper and illustrations before your answer to this letter has been received.

"Forssman's translation of chapters XX and XXI, in both draft and recopied versions, are enclosed herewith; Löfman has only made a few changes to them in pencil. Chapters XXII and XLV are being recopied.

"Countess Ericson has lived here in the capital for a couple of years and lives rather modestly with the exception of her residence, which, with 6 rooms and a kitchen for a rent of 2000 crowns seems to me much too grand for someone living in reduced circumstances; yet no matter how badly it may go for her, she will never become destitute, for her son-in-law Count Mörner is a wealthy landed proprietor.

"Carl was at my house last fall with a proposal that 10 of his friends, including me, each subscribe 6000 crowns to be combined in a loan to him, since he believed he could reach an agreement with Wenersborgs Enskilda Bank, who are his real creditors and could foreclose on him whenever they feel like it.

"To this loan proposal I had to reply first that I did not possess any capital to lend unless I were to take a loan myself, and as for his other friends, I suspected that they would be unwilling to make any more

sacrifices, since some years ago they had bought shares in the unfortunate papermaking plant when it was made into a publicly held company. The proposal was dropped, and Carl promised me an account of his financial position, not yet received.
With filial affection, Hj. Elworth[3]

Ericsson's rejoinder was swift. On the very same day, May 2, he received this letter, he sent a telegram to Hjalmar that made crisply clear his decision to cancel the Swedish edition. But he had already found that he could not manage to go back to business. The "mild words" cried out for what he felt should be a smashing rejoinder. He had sent it on the very same day, April 12, that Hjalmar was writing to ask him to reconsider.
"My dear Hjalmar,

Thanks for your letter of March 21. ...

"Your story about crossing out certain 'forceful expressions' etc., reinforces my satisfaction with the decision I have made in this matter. With reference to your saying that 'one's words should be mild if one's case is strong.' may I state quite plainly that the hammer is *my* weapon. Had I not learned to employ it well, I would long since have been in the poorhouse.
With warm affection, J. Ericsson
P.S. Kindly send Forssman's original – the recopying you mention is unnecessary. Why should F. 'complete the first chapters' after I have asked that all work be halted?"[4]

NOTES

1. Ericsson, John to Hjalmar Elworth, Mar. 22, 1878.
2. Elworth to Ericsson, Mar. 21, 1878.
3. Elworth to Ericsson, April 12, 1878.
4. Ericsson to Elworth, April 12, 1878.

CHAPTER 18

"The hammer is *my* weapon."

Remarkable, that John Ericsson, who, after the *U.S.S. Princeton* disaster, had been cheated both of reputation and of wages when Robert Stockton told the U.S. Navy the inventor was merely "an ingenious mechanic," should now write to his son that his chosen instrument was the most ordinary tool of the mechanic.

"The hammer is *my* weapon."

And that it was his chosen *weapon* for hand-to-hand combat, presumably (and risibly) with the "certain scientists" whose "experiments and findings" Ericsson "criticized" with what his son Hjalmar took to be "forceful expressions."

Except that John Ericsson's letter to Hjalmar was, as always, written in Swedish, and Ericsson's Swedish words, even more remarkable, were as follows: "*Släggan är* mitt *vapen.*"

Vapen certainly means 'weapon.' That is the translator's obvious first choice, though if Ericsson meant to characterize Science's process of peer review as hand-to-hand combat with weapons he was being, to say the least, melodramatic. But the second meaning of *vapen* is, the heraldic arms of a noble family, a "coat-of-arms."

"The hammer is *my* coat-of-arms."

John Ericsson had recently learned from Hjalmar what he called "the deplorable story of the fine gentlemen Ericson." The sudden downfall of Nils' heirs moved Nils' younger brother John to solicitude, but at the same time gave him a certain satisfaction. When Nils was elevated to the noble rank of baron and the new-minted aristocrat dropped one 's' from the family name, John had been so angry he threatened to disinherit Nils' children. Nils also had designed for himself a coat-of-arms, in which lock gates and a train wheel represented, respectively, his career accomplishments in building canals and in building railroads. Not irrelevant, then, if John meant to declare:

"The hammer is *my* coat-of-arms."

"*Släggan är* mitt *vapen.*"

Släggan means a sledgehammer, a two-handed hammer used, for example, by miners preparing for blasting. Son and grandson and great-grandson of miners and mine owners, John might have meant that this miner's tool was a more appropriate heraldic device for him than Nils' pretentious symbols, and that a hard-hitting prose style was more appropriate for him than lisping "mild words" to put his "strong case."[1]

Or perhaps he was reaching far back, all the way to ancient Norse mythology. As John would have known well since a child, the hammer *Mjölner* was hurled by the god *Thor* at any giant who dared oppose him. Thor's magical hammer never missed, and never failed to shatter whatever it struck. For an inventor who had so recently "succeeded in hurling out a body underwater at great speed, a problem that was generally considered insoluble," and that body a "torpedo," the Norse god Thor might well have seemed a role model.

Yes, the tale of Thor's hammer would have been among John Ericsson's earliest recollections, but there was still another terrible hammer in his earliest recollections. It had been wielded by the "sheriff" in Långbanshyttan. Each sharp stroke of his auction hammer took something away from their family home. Their table. Their chairs. Their pitcher. Their bowls.

Gone! Gone! Gone!

One after another, the icons in that intimate pantheon that forms a child's home, *gone*. And with them, this child's sense of safety. To John, that experience made the hammer the instrument of judgment. Never again would he submit mildly.

"The hammer is my *weapon."*

So Ericsson's several words weave a whole fabric of ambiguities. From this one phrase in his letter to Hjalmar, as through a prism, fan out some of his deepest values and motives like so many divergent rays.

Does his hammer metaphor still, in this context of translation, seem incongruous?

"The President of the United States declared it fitting that 'the completion of the first century of our national existence should be commemorated by an exhibition of the natural resources of the country and their development, and of its progress in those arts which benefit mankind.'"[2]

John Ericsson called himself "...the person who has done more to promote marine engineering, mechanical motors, implements of naval warfare, etc., than any other ten persons together during the last third of the lifetime of the American republic."[3]

But, unaccountably, he is rejected by the Centennial. "I have *five* times stood before an American jury - God knows, in all innocence - and five times the judgment has gone against me - this country's scientists are all against me, as are even the engineers, and every one of them, more or less, is a villain."[4]

Shocked, enraged at feeling himself judged again, once again as powerless as a small boy being banished from Långbanshyttan, John

Ericsson seized the hammer himself. *Contributions to the Centennial Exhibition* was written and illustrated and published and distributed around the world.

And just then Hjalmar came from Sweden and from his remotest past to see him. John Ericsson realized, as never before, that his own emotional life still resided in Sweden. A Swedish edition of his book! It would be a kind of bridge, across which he might find a way back.

Preoccupied with developing and testing a new weapon system, Ericsson put off reading the translated chapters of his book until half the book was done. Yet when at last he read the Swedish version Hjalmar's team of translators produced, he told his son that he "does not recognize" himself in it.Whom is it he does not recognize? A 23-year-old, embarking on ambition, just ransomed from those in Sweden who loved him by a wealth of promises he was never able to keep? Or a 73-year-old celebrity of invention whose dreadnought rhetoric in all the journals of engineering kept his critics, those villains, at bay?

"The forceful and convincing language that has placed me among our times' leading English writers...has quite simply [been] murdered," Ericsson wrote his son. He had made his choice.

What better tool than a sledgehammer to demolish a bridge?

"New York, May 3, 1878
My dear Hjalmar,

Thank you for your letter of April 12 along with three issues of *Dagligt Allehanda.* Immediately on receiving the letter I addressed your most important question by telegram.

"I am surprised in the highest degree that you did not know that *Handels Tidningen*, Sweden's largest daily newspaper, had published a story about the book you are [*sic*] translating (a story that then became a general topic of conversation all over the country) and this reinforces my conclusion that you know very little about what is going on in Sweden. I am now able to understand why you did not let me know anything about the ongoing tests of the Whitehead torpedo aboard the torpedo boat *Ran*, etc. That it is a matter of highest importance for me, now, when I am sacrificing all my time to the torpedo matter and to Swedish naval defense, to receive information about what is happening, I hardly need remind you.

"The enclosed selection from the New York newspaper *The Sun* I ask you to translate and publish in *Dagligt Allehanda* if its editor considers the subject important enough to be given a prominent place in his newspaper.

"Unexpected matters force me to interrupt this letter before I have said what I intended when I took up my pen.
"With warm affection,
J. Ericsson"[5]

After the unexpected interruption that left his intention hanging over the letter like a cloud, Ericsson nevertheless found the time to have his secretary, S.W. Taylor, copy the letter in a fair hand before dispatching it.

On the very same day, Hjalmar was writing from Stockholm:
"My dear Father,

From your telegram received last night I learn with disappointment that you have decided irrevocably your book will not be printed here. I had no way of knowing that the quick return of the paper was so urgent, and so I ask your pardon for the delay caused by the proposal I made in my last letter – a proposal offered with the best intentions.

"However, in accordance with the instructions received in your letter of mid-April, I tried to get the needed documents from the customs house here, but it did not prove possible because the cases had been transshipped in Hull. I then spoke with the American consul, Col. Elfwing, who promised me the certificate needed for customs-free reentry in return for my giving my word that the contents of the cases were the same as on arrival, and [he] also promised the certified invoice in triplicate, of which one copy stays with the cases, one is transmitted via Elfwing to the customs house in New York, and the third is turned over to me to be forwarded directly to you.

"The smaller case with the typefaces and the copy of the book separately bound by chapters is being sent by the same means as the paper and illustrations, that is, by rail to Gothenburg and then in the care of Wilson's via Hull to New York. That case will require payment of customs charges, as proper documentation of when and how it was sent here is lacking.

"Your letter of April 12 arrived here on the 30th of the month. I hope that the copies of newspapers containing the torpedo articles have arrived quickly. That I sent clippings earlier was only for the convenience of enclosing them in ordinary letters. I have 10 copies of the printed Chapter I that will be kept very securely or, perhaps better, burned.

"Before your counter-order arrived, Forssman had already translated chapters XXIII-XXVI of the book's mechanical section, and I enclose these along with the book's final chapter. These five drafts are entirely in the same condition as received from Forssman. Chapter XXII, which had a great many things crossed out and written in, was sent out for recopying a long time ago, and I hope to be able to send you that within a couple of days. Along with this letter I am sending Chapters II-VII in three separate covers. Forssman's draft accompanies chapters II-V, but the drafts of VI and VII should still be in your hands.

"As soon as those involved have submitted their final bills I will send you my accounts for the money received. Probably the balance remaining will amount to 2,000 crowns.

"Sophie sends you her warm greetings."[6]

In four days Hjalmar wrote again, this time more briefly, to notify his father that the paper and illustrations were on their way to Gothenburg.

It was the end of May before he wrote his father again, and then he had (with a certain relief, one can imagine) been away on railroad business.

"My dear Father,

"I received your letter of the 3rd yesterday on my return from a week's inspection trip on the Southern lines. The article from *The Sun* that came with it I will translate without delay. Dr. Lindström, when I called on him just now, declared that he would gratefully accept your article for *Dagligt Allehanda.* He took occasion to mention that a series of articles on the Russian torpedo conditions is to be published in his paper very soon. Concerning torpedo trials aboard the *Ran* mine boat, he knew nothing and to the best of my knowledge no story about them has yet appeared. However, at my earliest opportunity I shall try to find any news of these trials.

"Concerning your remark that Gothenburg's *Handels och Sjöfartstidningen* is Sweden's largest daily paper, I would like to mention that it is not so regarded here, nor is it read very much in the capital. Even in Gothenburg the *Göteborgsposten* competes with it. Our biggest papers doubtless are *Dagligt Allehanda* and *Aftonbladet* . Chiefly from the former of these I gain what I know about events and happenings – beyond that, I have little time over for newspaper reading.

"I am now on the point of departure and my inspection trips are going to last very nearly three months, though now and then during this period I will be coming home and dealing with my correspondence.

"I have gotten into a row in the papers with Professor Edlund because he recommends several electrical railroad signal devices patented by a Joh. Brunius, but after putting the devices through our official testing I have had to declare them unsuitable for our climate."[7]

This last of the May letters from Hjalmar makes quite a different impression from the earlier two, which in their handwriting betray the heavy pressure his father's May 2 telegram placed on him. Now, writing his father almost a month later, his handwriting and his tone seem to have become firmer, if also less spontaneous and open than in previous months. In truth, he must have begun to appreciate his escape from the demands of the translation project. Yet he is still responsive. Finally he has a father. He is not ready to be written off.

Ericsson, in the letter he mails to Hjalmar at the end of the month, almost seems to have been relieved by hurling his "hammer." The handwriting here is the inventor's own:

"Dear Hjalmar:

Your welcome letters of May 3 and 7, along with the documents you mention, have reached me. Prof. Edlund's negligence cannot be satisfactorily explained. I regret that people give me so little encouragement in my native land. My basic research into the temperature of the sun at various distances from its center is one of the most important events of our time. Shame on our scientists who have not uttered a word on the subject.

"Taylor received the documents you sent him in the usual time – we are now awaiting the arrival of the cases. For heaven's sake do not go to the trouble of sending me the invoices – if, as you anticipate, a sum of 2,000 crowns remains, I want you to regard it as your own. Use it for translation of newspaper articles etc. I count on your covering the expense. The machinery for my new torpedo boat is almost ready and so far meets my expectations. The vessel is not as ready to take the water as I had planned – however, everything will be ready to be tested in good time.

"By all means send me every story you can find about the results of trials with the Whitehead torpedoes in Swedish hands. Also would you please send me a copy of Commodore Adlersparre's treatise on *Materials for Today's Naval Warfare.*

Judging by the excerpts published in the *Handels Tidning*, my friend has committed some dreadful blunders.

"Do not send me the remaining chapters of the book's practical section – more about this on another occasion.

"Convey my hearty greetings to Sophie.

With warm affection,

J. Ericsson"[8]

NOTES

1. "During the construction of an engine, a certain casting appearing to him doubtful as to soundness, Ericsson...insisted on having it broken on the spot. Some stalwart workmen accordingly attacked it with...sledges, but, failing to make an impression, they desisted at length, saying: 'We will put it under the drop by and by.' His quick temper rose at this, but he spoke not a word; with his right hand he snatched the sledge from the nearest man and in an instant it whirled like a meteor before the eyes of the astonished spectators, the ponderous tool driving its head at the first stroke through the shell of the

dubious casting... He tossed away the sledge as if it had been a jack straw, and turning on his heel, strode away with the remark: 'Now you *may* put it under the drop.'" *Scientific American*, Dec. 14, 1889, in Church, William C., 1906, i, 135-6.

2. Gen. Joseph Hawley, president of the Centennial Commission, in Trout, S.E., 1929, 128.
3. Ericsson, John to Axel Adlersparre, 1876, in Church, 1907, ii, 183.
4. Ericsson to Adlersparre, April 25, 1876.
5. Ericsson, John to Hjalmar Elworth, May 3, 1878.
6. Elworth to Ericsson, May 3, 1878.
7. Elworth to Ericsson, May 29, 1878. He may also have begun to suffer a chronic health condition. At the end of the 1870s, through his nephew John Ericson [the inventor] learned that Hjalmar's wife Sophie had told the nephew about Hjalmar's 'gallstones or something.' So Hjalmar was only 53 years old when he began to have problems with his health." Runvik, Margaretha, 1996, 149.
8. Ericsson to Elworth, May 30, 1878.

V

In the Black

CHAPTER 19

Sophie Elworth was sick again.

Hjalmar had set out on a series of railroad inspection trips soon after John Ericsson gave up on a forceful Swedish version of his *Contributions to the Centennial Exhibition* and canceled the project. The possibility that his father might now abandon him anew must have crossed his mind. But Hjalmar must also have been relieved to turn his whole attention once again to the demanding work of managing all the machines and facilities of the Swedish railroad system.

But when Hjalmar returned from one of these trips just before Midsummer Day 1878 he found Sophie once more in pain, as he wrote his father.

"...I must offer my deep gratitude for your gift of the remaining [book translation project] funds. This sum I am going to put aside for a stay in Karlsbad for my poor Sophie, who has once again had an attack of her previous complaint, caused by gallstones. This affliction, which is intensely painful and usually lasts 5 or 6 days, has just passed for now, thank God. Sophie is undergoing a cure here in Stockholm, but should it not succeed, the doctor says Karlsbad will be her only remaining recourse."

And there was that gift from Ericsson of 3,000 francs for their trip together:

"At the beginning of September I hope to take leave so that we can make our trip to Paris."[1]

Sophie would survive her husband by almost 35 years, and yet during these years of stress between father and son, it is as though Sophie's health served as a barometer of the weather prevailing between Ericsson and Hjalmar. Perhaps she was reflecting emotions that Hjalmar was not allowed to express. No one can doubt her own deep emotional involvement in the difficult relationship between father and son, even from the very first.

Sophie and Hjalmar had become engaged in 1855, when she was 21 and he, then foreman of construction on a canal that traverses Härnösand, her home town, was 31 years old. A letter Nils wrote to Hjalmar at that time cautions the young man on the marital responsibilities he is about to undertake but also promises him a job on Nils' new railroad project.

Nils had succeeded the late Baltzar von Platen as the nation's premier canal builder. So outstanding had been Nils' direction of the Trollhätte canal project – completed in 1844 a year before schedule and with some savings below budget – that he had been entrusted by the king with responsibility of directing construction of the new and already controversial Swedish national railroad network.

At the wedding in September 1855, Sophia Magdalena Fahlman had been given away by her father, Carl Robert Fahlman, a prominent merchant of Härnösand, and her mother Christina Magdalena. But on Hjalmar's side of the aisle neither mother nor father was to be seen. Nor even named.

Yet his uncle Nils and his wife Wilhelmina probably attended, with their sons John, Werner and Carl and daughter Hedda, cousins whom Hjalmar liked to think of as his boyhood companions, even though his name set him apart.

Sophie was bravely marrying a made-up name and a secret.

Hjalmar Elworth thrived in the railroad project, certainly with a debt to Nils' encouragement, but it is clear that he had ability. He advanced from Southern Line station engineer in 1855 to district engineer on the Western Line in 1857, to traffic director of the Södertälje branch in 1860, where he supervised the construction of a key railroad tunnel and two swing-bridges. Soon Elworth was appointed to supervise the first traffic district, connecting the national capital Stockholm to Hallsberg and, in 1863, right after Nils retired, he was made a member of the Governing Board of the system. By 1866 Hjalmar headed two departments, in charge of machines and facilities.[2]

It was from the trajectory of Hjalmar's rapid rise that Sophie Elworth wrote, secretly, to John Ericsson at the end of 1868, apparently for the second time: "Some years ago I wrote to you begging that you would write a few kind words to Hjalmar. You have certainly proved that you have not forgotten him, and he owes his education, which has enabled him to reach an independent position, to you; but all you have given him is through others and never yet has a kind word from you gladdened his heart. He cannot but believe that he is quite an indifferent person to you. I was confirmed in this belief when no answer to my former letter ever came, but I have also been thinking that it might never have reached you. I have heard so much about your benevolence and kindness to even the meanest of your countrymen. Why then this indifference toward us?

"I beg you again to let me, your son's wife, know if you wish the relation between us to remain for the future as it has been. Your wish in this case will be a law to me, but I beg to assure you that a kind word would make us happy beyond description. I preserve some old letters from you to your mother (our grandmother). I have just read them again and the feeling you there express encourages me to make this last attempt. Should I fail, Hjalmar will never know it. However you act toward us you will always be to us, as to every Swede, dear and precious. Maybe it is pardonable if from the height where you are one forgets many things that otherwise would be sweet."[3]

Was it Sophie Elworth's firm but gentle pressure that finally induced Hjalmar's father to open the door, if ever so slightly, to direct communication between them? Or was it Ericsson's shockingly sudden bereavement, within two weeks in 1870, of both his sister Anna Carolina and his brother Nils, leaving him the sole survivor of his generation? "Emotions overwhelm me," he wrote, and had to put his pen away.

Still, it was the end of 1872 before Hjalmar received in the mail, on his birthday, a New York newspaper clipping about his father's measurement of the sun. Hjalmar, seizing his pen and what he took to be his opportunity, wrote for the first time in his 48 years "Dear Father..." It was a letter signed "Hjalmar" about whose answer we have to speculate. Nothing we have, signed by Ericsson during the period 1872 to 1876, seems to have been directed to his son. For all we know, Hjalmar's only answer was still another clipping; just at that time Ericsson was producing a great many technical articles published in a variety of journals and papers. And such ephemera would have crumbled to dust by now.

But now, almost six eventful years after the son's first letter and two years after their last meeting in New York, Hjalmar wrote his father that "Sophie...seems now to be entirely recovered and is continuing with her cure. However, our trip to Paris cannot be undertaken earlier than October, since during September I have several duties to perform for two new sections of rail in northern Sweden... at [one of] which H.M. the King will be present." He adds that these northern tracts are well known to his father, and so he is sending along a little sketch map on which he has marked the new routes in red.[4]

Several weeks later Hjalmar has just returned from opening a new railway between Visby and Hemse on the island of Gotland. "The celebrations turned out especially well and were visited by H.M. the King, who traveled there on the mine-boat *Ran*." Hjalmar remembered that Ericsson considered this boat the leading rival to his own torpedo-launching *Destroyer*, and made sure to look it over thoroughly, so that he could send a description that is comprehensive. He concludes: "Sophie is now well... Around the 8th of October we plan to take our Paris trip, and to be away a month."[5]

But in mid-October he has to write:

"Week after week hindered by things piling up, at last I am going to travel tomorrow to Paris, unfortunately alone, because Sophie has recently had an attack of her sickness and does not dare to venture out.

Next spring it will probably be necessary for her to go to Karlsbad, and after that, the trip she has now missed might be undertaken..."

But he has other, more dramatic news to relate, concerning the economic hardships of Nils' family:

"There has been great disquiet in the Ericson family. John, who has leased out Nygård for a long time, is still living there, but recently has had to sell most of his best furniture. Carl has sold Rannum and received such a good price that he is now debt-free, and on the first of this month moved to Lidköping, planning to scrape by with his Captain's pay (about 2,000 crowns), which will be difficult even though he has a good and prudent wife.

"The only thing anyone knows about Werner is that he is out of the country, but not where, neither does anybody know what he is living on.

"The countess lives here in the city and has succeeded in renting out some furnished rooms in her apartment, so that she lives in what is left over, for the sake of some hundreds of crowns."[6]

At the beginning of December he writes his father that "My trip to Paris was especially pleasant and the exposition very interesting, even though there was hardly anything new in railroad equipment to be seen. ... Sophie is now, thank God, well and cheerful."[7]

Ericsson ends 1878 with a long letter to Hjalmar.

"Thank you for your letter containing Frykholm's account [of Swedish tests of the Whitehead torpedo, chief competitor of Ericsson's design]. ... Pity our homeland if better defenses should not exist – even if the torpedo was capable, the torpedo boat (a *Ran*) can be sunk with a single shot!

"Your translation, published in *Dagligt Allehanda* on September 21, was erroneous on one important point...

"Allow me to remind you that I am an engineer and constructor, more than an inventor. How improper to call my torpedo vessel, with its manifold mechanical arrangements, an 'invention.' Edison, in the depths of his ignorance, hits upon things, or invents. Ericsson, on familiar terms with the laws of physics, constructs. *Dagligt Allehanda* calls the *Destroyer* 'Ericsson's newest invention.' *Allehanda för Folket*, quite rightly, calls the ship 'Ericsson's latest naval weapon.' Do you know what the latter newspaper has to say on the subject? If so, why do you not, in keeping with my repeated pleadings, send me the paper? When you write me again, please let me know whether any Swedish newspaper copied the September 21 article in *Dagligt Allehanda*. ...

"I am not in the least surprised at Sweden, since I know full well the dangerous foundations on which the country's large national income has recently rested, as well as the unsound sources from which they have taken money for the many unnecessary railroads. Thus what lies in store for our dear homeland during the coming decade I foresee quite completely. The punishment will be harsh but healthful for our national spirit. My dear countrymen will be reminded that a human being can be happy without being surrounded by luxury. ...

"If any article concerning my torpedo boat should be published in *Allehanda för Folket* I wish it, through your kind offices, to be inserted into *Dagligt*

[*A gap exists in the letter.*]

With the greatest happiness I learn that Sophie is well once more. Give her my hearty greetings. ..."

All of the above is in Samuel Taylor's stately hand, but the P.S. is in Ericsson's own impelled scrawl: "To advance the good cause I wish you immediately to translate and publish in *Dagligt Allehanda* the enclosed article from Army and Navy Journal – by all means omit the crossed-out stupid paragraph."[8]

This lecture, these complaints, and these peremptory demands may actually have reassured Hjalmar. His father intended to go on as before, Swedish *Contributions* book or not.

NOTES

1. Elworth, Hjalmar to John Ericsson, June 24, 1878.
2. By 1870, when Nils died, Hjalmar Elworth was one of the three "Överdirektör" executives managing the whole system. "The technical progress the national railways made under his direction was significant," according to the leading Swedish biographical reference, *Svenska Biografiska Lexikon*, ranking Hjalmar right after Nils Ericson, and today Nils Ericson's statue still stands at the entrance to Stockholm's imposing Central Station, while Nils' full-length oil portrait hangs in the grand council chamber of the Swedish Railways' board of directors.
3. Elworth, Sophie to John Ericsson, Dec. 28, 1868 in White, Ruth, 1960, 237.
4. Elworth to Ericsson, Aug. 25, 1878.
5. Elworth to Ericsson, Sept. 13, 1878.
6. Elworth to Ericsson, Oct. 12, 1878.
7. Elworth to Ericsson, Dec. 4, 1878.
8. Ericsson to Elworth, Dec. 27, 1878.

CHAPTER 20

Over the years the relations between father and son gradually manifested some changes, especially in John Ericsson.

As early as February of 1879, Ericsson told his son that his translation of an article in *Army and Navy Journal* "was truly excellent," though he continued: "By all means send me the...speeches in Parliament about any aspect of naval defense. As you know, I now devote nearly full time and substantial resources to the matter. Is it necessary, then, to explain the necessity of learning everything that happens in this connection?"

But his father's next few lines may have come as a surprise to Hjalmar, they were so reasonable: "Should you yourself not have time to keep up with everything that is happening, I request that you immediately use some suitable person to do so. I will be pleased to cover all expenses. I cannot criticize your being so concentrated on [the duties of] your position that you have no time to keep up with what happens, but the situation is unlucky for me, who incautiously dismissed my previous correspondents."[1]

In March of the same year, C. L. Adelsköld, an author, sent John Ericsson a biography of his late brother. This made John Ericsson aware that some kind of autobiographical statement by Nils also existed, and he telegraphed Hjalmar in April asking him to obtain it.

"I have searched for Uncle Nils' autobiography," Hjalmar replied, "But nothing of the kind exists except for the very brief one he submitted, as required, on his admission to the Academy of Sciences. From this I have had the enclosed copy made.

Yesterday I met Adelsköld and received the life story he wrote on assignment from the Academy, a copy of which he recently sent to you. He then told me that, some years ago, when he was planning to write this life story, he first sent you a letter asking for information about your early years, but received no reply. Therefore he turned to Gustaf Ekman, who seems to have known you both in your youth, and from him received some information he used almost word-for-word in writing the life story in question."[2]

"Since Adelsköld's lie has been published in the Proceedings of the National Academy of Sciences and so has been spread all over Scandinavia," Ericsson wrote back in May, "I request that you immediately print the enclosed statements [" *Excerpt from a letter regarding the Ericsson family* "] in quarto format under my name... I need not add that you should then distribute this 'excerpt' in the

Nordic countries among educated people and the leading educational institutions. I am tired of the eternal chatter that I came out of a peasant's cottage, when actually from earliest childhood I was surrounded only by educated people – my father despised low company and could not even bear the smell of a peasant.

"...Let me mention in the strictest confidence that quite recently I received a letter from the King, *personally*, which allows me to suppose that H.M. approves my *Destroyer* system. The details, he says, 'seem to me and all the professionals here in Sweden to be worked out with the utmost brilliance.' I refrain from giving you the entire contents of this flattering letter, which near its conclusion goes like this: 'Your fatherland, beloved of us both, shall accept with gratitude still another costly contribution to its defense at the moment of danger!' etc. etc.

"Before you print my letter, I ask that you allow Adelsköld to read it. Just possibly, some brief forgiving paragraph might be put into it for his benefit, but not as though I had written it myself.

"I regret that my late brother's memory is going to suffer, but the penalty for his injustice to and lack of respect for a lovable and upright father could not be put off forever."[3]

Hjalmar, who was indebted to Nils for so much, must have found this reproach hard to take. But, reading on, he must have realized that at last he had a direct answer to his plea, in the first letter he ever wrote to his father in 1872, to know more about him. There was more about Nils' early life, too.

The *Excerpt* begins by thanking an unnamed correspondent for Nils Ericson's autobiographical statement and also the biography written by Major Adelsköld, "It is with regret that I have read both...because they are incorrect in several respects and moreover they reflect on my father, who is supposed to have neglected the upbringing of his sons."

Nils' own narrative says unequivocally that the Ericsson boys received "only what education could be given us by our mother."[4] John's vigorous contradiction, some 1500 words in length, enumerated a series of efforts by Olof, from their arrival at the canal headquarters in Forsvik, to buy, borrow or beg instruction for his sons. Olof, he said, hired a governess and then after her a live-in tutor, he gave a fellow employee board at his table in return for teaching his sons, he persuaded a transient professional to give his boys intensive if brief training while in town; he tried every possible combination of improvisation and ingenuity to get them whatever expertise could be got. And Olof was himself no mean teacher.

"My father wrote a handsome hand, was an excellent bookkeeper and could do calculations with unusual facility. He had a naturally keen judgment in mechanical matters and was a great admirer of [Christopher]

Polhem. Before I was 11 years of age he had taught me, among other things, to construct an ellipse and shown me how, by using a ball in the joints of machines, to overcome the difficulties associated with varying angles of movement."

What Hjalmar was losing from the image of his uncle he was gaining in a positive image of the grandfather who had died 6 years before he was born. But there were other losses ahead.

"That my mother 'contributed to the support of the family by feeding the workers' is not true; my father's salary was sufficient to make such a recourse unnecessary," John Ericsson continued. "It is true they were able to persuade her to prepare meals for the administrators and the officers in charge of the [troops who built the canal] at Forsvik Station in the years 1811 and 1812. She took on this assignment more as a hostess than a proprietor, with the unhappy result that, at the end of two years my father had gone deeply into debt with the merchants of Mariestad, who delivered the great stock of groceries, etc., that the groaning board in the Forsvik headquarters called for. After my father passed on in 1818...my mother agreed once again to provide meals at several stations for those officers commanding the workers, but always with substantial losses because her table was too generously furnished.

"Since this was noticed, my mother obtained permission to brew and sell drinks to the troops. In this way she not only made good the losses at her table but even earned enough extra to pay off the debts her hospitality in Forsvik had caused. I remember quite well how the sensitive wife, after settling these debts, proudly related to me that she had just sent the last payment to her husband's creditors. 'No one shall ever again be able,' she said, 'to humiliate me with reminders that they have lost [money] on the departed.' It should be mentioned that, after my father's job as foreman at Hajtorp station was abolished, he was hired at Känsö quarantine station, where his death occurred in the summer of 1818 after a long illness in the care of my mother..."[5]

Brita Sofia Ericsson had brought into Hjalmar's young life the only mothering presence he ever experienced. John Ericsson's exposure of his mother's petty maneuver to shift blame to her departed spouse could not have been congenial to Hjalmar.

Nevertheless, Hjalmar translated the *Excerpt* into Swedish, and wrote his father that "the account of the Ericsson family will be published as you wish. As for the distribution of this account, it really should not extend any wider than the members of the Academy since Uncle Nils' [auto]biography, that your account censures, is not any official document but only a working paper that remains within the Academy. It was only through special contacts that I was allowed to read and take a copy of it. Neither is Adelsköld's printed work made for the general public, instead it is only distributed to members of the Academy and perhaps a few closer friends and relations of Uncle Nils.

"However, your account is interesting and ought to be distributed to the public, but in that case the passages concerning the biographies written by Uncle Nils and Adelsköld should not remain, seeing as the public has no knowledge of these biographies."[6]

Ericsson accepted Elworth's point of view, only asking to see the revision in advance. "As far as I have been told," he wrote, "the general opinion in Sweden is that the Ericssons' upbringing was neglected. This situation cannot be overlooked in the writing you plan."[7]

Hjalmar responded in August by giving his father a list of Swedish publications he had persuaded to print Ericsson's revised *Excerpt.*

Once more he relayed personal news of Nils' family: "Carl Ericson has recently lost his little son. This is now the third child he has lost," and "probably Baron John will be forced to sell Nygård.

"What would you say," he asked his father, "to buying the place? In these times it could not be sold for more than 200,000 crowns, and it really is worth that."[8]

John Ericsson's response to this offer was swift and succinct: "I realize that 200,000 crowns is a low price for Nygård, but my resources are never going to be used in such a way."[9]

"You have heard by telegram," John Ericsson wrote his son at the beginning of December, "how pleased I am with the translation in *Nya Dagligt Allehanda.* The article in *Familjejournalen* is also, thanks to your corrections, very good." The sentence that follows is the first hint in all their extant letters that Hjalmar had taken on an entirely new role: "The enclosed copy of my letter to the Minister of Naval Defense I send you in the strictest confidence, so that you may see how matters stand and so be able to negotiate appropriately for my benefit."[10]

"My dear Hjalmar," John Ericsson wrote, as the year 1879 drew to a close, "with sorrow and shame I have received the letter from Consul C.E. Södling I enclose. Please write to Mr. S.A. Svalander and ask him, in all kindness, to set up such a sturdy marker on my father's grave that it cannot be displaced through the winter.

"Meanwhile I ask you to order from Gothenburg a grave stone of granite with a simple, suitable inscription. As I know neither the day nor the year of his birth, you will have to find the correct dates in the Värmland parish records. The good man's date of death must be known to the family.

"Allow me to note that I do not by any means wish a *monument* – it is a simple grave stone (half its length strongly fastened below the ground) I wish you to erect.

Kindly send me in advance a drawing that shows your considered proposal.
"With warm affection,
J. Ericsson
"Please mail me at once the issue of the *Review of the Royal Academy of Sciences* that contains a paper by Jonas Wenström concerning a new law of radiation, or some such title."[11]

In a month, Hjalmar returned this report:

"Regarding the grave stone mentioned earlier, the situation is this. Uncle Nils long ago entrusted Svalander, who had been the cashier of the quarantine station on Känsö, with placing a grave cross and promised to send him one. But no such cross was ever heard of, so that finally Svalander reminded John [Ericson, Nils' son] about it. Then an iron cross inscribed "Olof Ericsson, Construction Inspector during the construction of the Känsö Quarantine Facility" was shipped over and in 1878 set up on the little hill that encloses his remains.

"Thus Consul Södling has gone to a great deal of unnecessary trouble, but he can be excused because when he visited Känsö the cross had not yet arrived, but only came immediately afterward, according to Svalander.

"Learning from your letter that you lack Grandfather's birth and death dates, I enclose a family tree of the Ericsson and Yngström families like the one I took down from Grandmother's dictation and later completed.
"With filial affection,
Hj. Elworth"[12]

"I received your letter...with a satisfaction I cannot describe," his father wrote back. "Thank you for the family tree, it was especially welcome."[13]

Hjalmar had already written of a general financial crisis in Sweden, and now he told his father that it had affected the leadership of the national railway:

"Here, hard times continue in the business world. Hofors and Hammarby, among other industrial companies, have gone under, leaving a debt of 7 million crowns. My chief, General Director Troilius, had his whole fortune invested in them and now will probably have to leave his position. A couple of provincial newspapers have already named me his successor, but of this there has not been any question whatsoever, nor would I be able from an economic standpoint to take the job."

In Hjalmar's next paragraph there is a curious echo from Hjalmar's very first letter to his father nine years before:

"It is true that my current salary is no more than 7,000 crowns, but as an experienced railway builder I am often retained to give engineering-related advice to the independent railroad companies, and in this way I earn another 4 to 5 thousand crowns a year. The director's salary is 10,000 but the position brings along with it various representation costs and would exclude any possibility of the extra assignments I mentioned. Thus my situation would be worsened, not to mention having to take on the great responsibility and all the aggravation that comes with leading the management of a great railroad."

The crisis had consequences even closer to home: "The Ericson family has had a hard time. Nygård was advertised for sale at executive auction for a debt to the Wenersborg Bank, but fortunately was bought just in time by John's brother-in-law, the landowner A. Kock, for 230,000 crowns, so that John can probably stay on. Werner seems to have been in London to promote an invention that achieves great economy of fuel through the use of superheated steam. However, in England it does not seem to catch on; how would it be if he came over to America?"[14]

A telegram John Ericsson sent was meant to avert that. A letter followed:

"I presume that Werner now knows, through John, based on my telegram to you, that I do not like his invention, and I urge him not to come here with his crazy notions. It is lamentable that Werner is so ill-informed about the laws of motion as his invention attests. His contraption runs so counter to common sense that engineers who look at his drawing and read his pompous description would find it difficult not to laugh out loud.

"Thank you for the *Review*, which has come in good time."[15]

"I take it for granted," Ericsson repeated in his next letter, "that Werner now knows my views about his invention. ... I would regard his arrival here as a great misfortune for me – my worries and sacrifices for my countrymen would, in case he comes here, really trouble me. What you say about an oversupply of engineers in Sweden bodes no good for me, since when all else fails they come to me. That is how matters have stood for more than 30 years."[16]

But the dreaded nephew had not, or said he had not, heard of John Ericsson's views.

"Werner Ericsson is here," John Ericsson wrote Hjalmar some months later. "Despite the relevant messages I sent you in ample time. He assured me on his arrival a week ago that he was ignorant of my advice in the matter, but now he has received letters addressed from New York that made it plain I had advised against his coming. ... Werner's presence here is going to disturb my life, since I find him entirely ignorant of engineering – he cannot make even the simplest mechanical drawing! I thank God that my brother gave *you* a better education."[17]

NOTES

1. Ericsson, John to Hjalmar Elworth, Feb. 21, 1879.
2. Elworth to Ericsson, Apr. 26, 1879.
3. Ericsson to Elworth, May 23, 1879.
4. Ericson, Nils, 1845, 1.
5. Ericsson, John, 1879.
6. Elworth to Ericsson, Jun. 21, 1879.
7. Ericsson to Elworth, Jul. 18, 1879.
8. Elworth to Ericsson, Aug. 10, 1879.
9. Ericsson to Elworth, Sep. 5, 1879.
10. Ericsson to Elworth, Dec. 5, 1879.
11. Ericsson to Elworth, Dec. 12, 1879.
12. Elworth to Ericsson, Jan. 12, 1880.
13. Ericsson to Elworth, Feb. 13, 1880.
14. Elworth to Ericsson, Dec. 26, 1879.
15. Ericsson to Elworth, Feb. 13, 1880.
16. Ericsson to Elworth, Apr. 2, 1880.
17. Ericsson to Elworth, Nov. 12, 1880. A couple of weeks later, Ericsson wrote directly to Werner: "I refuse to throw away my time by further discussion [of your invention]. I shall, however, be most happy to see you at all times (by preference at 6 p.m.) if you will take the trouble to drop me a line the day before." - Nov. 29, 1880.

CHAPTER 21

Near the close of 1880 John Ericsson wrote Hjalmar again for help:

"The enclosed letter to Werner Ericson, I ask you to translate and give to John, who will then let his mother and brother read it. This will let the family know how I am treating this inexperienced engineer. I still do not know whether Werner is going to return to Europe, or what support he is going to need. ... P.S. ... I have written a second letter to Werner, the result of an interview last night."[1]

Two weeks later, with increasing pessimism:

"I enclose still another letter to Werner Ericson, the contents of which you will kindly communicate to his mother and brothers so that they may know the present situation of this stubborn and conceited man. God knows how it will end – in discomfort for me, certainly."[2]

But he wrote more optimistically a week after that:

"It is a pleasure to tell you that my last letter to Werner Ericson of December 14 persuaded him to refrain from troubling me further with demonstrations and calculations meant to prove the correctness of his fancied improvement to the steam engine.

"To soften the sting of disappointed hopes, I undertook to give him, on that condition, an allowance of $100 dollars a month for one year – in accordance with the copy I enclose of a letter from my secretary.[3] With this support, something over 6,000 francs a year, I hope Werner will be enabled to equip himself for making a living.

"It makes me especially happy to reciprocate in this way the kindness his father showed you, without which you would not have reached the position in society you now hold. As for my brother's cash outlays for you, as you know he received timely reimbursement for them, plus interest.

"With warm affection, J. Ericsson

"P.S. ... You may let the family know that Werner is in good hands. ... "[4]

He was being asked to convey these papers and the news of his father's persistent efforts to help Werner to his cousin's mother and brothers. Hjalmar seems always to have communicated regularly with Nils' son John, who at this time was a member of the parliament. It must have been tempting merely to send Ericsson's letters over to John, and so fulfill the letter of his father's instructions. But, instead, Hjalmar decided to call upon Nils' widow, Wilhelmina, Countess von Schwerin, personally, with Ericsson's several letters expressing great impatience with her son.

It was a delicate mission. He would first have sent her a note from his apartment in the new Stockholm Central Station, one of the parade apartments Nils, before his retirement, had arranged for his triumvirate of successors in the direction of the railway system. Hjalmar's note would ask for a convenient time to call on her. He knew, and she knew that he knew, her reply came from another grand apartment now sadly subdivided so that she could rent rooms to eke out a living income. He was asking to come and see her in surroundings of which she was no longer proud. He would be bringing her Ericsson's pessimistic letters, some containing "forceful expressions" critical of Werner.

Werner was the son for whom Nils had cherished hopes that Hjalmar, instead, fulfilled. When Nils' eldest son, John, opted for politics and youngest, Carl, for military life, Werner was educated to be an engineer. When a Dalsland canal was to be constructed, Nils, by then retired, passed the leading role to neophyte Werner. The son asked his father for help with every phase, and Nils sent him fifty detailed letters over 1865-6, often enclosing sketches, and also visited to inspect the progress of the work.

There are reasons to believe that Nils realized Werner's limitations. But on completion in 1868, the canal was considered a great success for both of them, and brought Werner a handsome fee. It was this money that launched the paper pulp mill project he and his brothers conceived, and made Werner its Director.[5]

But Werner's deficiencies soon affected the enterprise, already floundering because the number of mills multiplied even as the market for pulp contracted, and then Nils' death in 1870 deprived him of vital advice. That he began to disappear for long periods did not help the situation. Eventually Wilhelmina must have understood that besides his technical deficiencies her second son had other troubles.

It can be doubted that Werner's mother felt any special affection for the nephew whose talents had outshone her own son's. Their relations may well have been distant and formal. Neither had she made any attempt to maintain contact with Nils' brother in America. Yet now her troubled son was dependent on the kindness of this American stranger Ericsson whom Hjalmar had actually met and spent some time with. She must have been curious.

The outcome of Hjalmar's call on Wilhelmina we can decipher from a much- reworked draft of the letter Hjalmar sent his father early in 1881.

"The copies of your letters to Werner that you sent me I translated immediately and carried to his mother, who was deeply disappointed about the [illegible] man's behavior...She asked me to send you her cordial greeting and her gratitude for what you have done for Werner.

She said that she would write him personally at once and set him straight."[6]

Meantime, Hjalmar had not simply filed and forgotten his transcontinental observations in America. A month later, Hjalmar wrote his father about a subject he had first taken up with him nine years before, his quest for an effective snow plow to deploy on the Swedish railways:

"This year we have an especially snowy winter and almost all month I have been out on the line to look at the snowdrifts and figure out how they can be overcome. For this, a just-completed snow plow designed by the Pacific Railway has proved excellent. I obtained the drawings for it in San Francisco and when I got home spent my spare evenings making a model of it. This now serves as a pattern for construction of the plow.

"In the trials I used up to 3 locomotives behind the plow and went through drifts 8 or 9 feet high, 600 feet long. Similar plows are now going to be built for all the districts of the national railways."[7]

"That you have succeeded with your snow plow pleases me in the highest degree," his father replied in March. "As you have not yet mentioned my letter of December 24 I take it for granted that it has not yet arrived. I have just now completed the working drawings of what is going to become the world's fastest steam engine, intended for generating electrical lights – [it develops] 10 horse power, its speed 1,000 revolutions a minute."[8]

By mid-April, Hjalmar reports: "Your letter of December 24 arrived in due time and right away I communicated its contents to Countess Ericson, who seemed very grateful for the support you have provided Werner."[9]

Early the next month Ericsson acknowledged a letter from Countess Ericson:

"My dear Wilhelmina,

Receiving a letter from you brought me more pleasure than you can imagine; but since it undoubtedly has been my duty to write you first, I felt some reproach at first sight of your welcome letter. The reason I am so late in answering is that during this time I believed Werner might possibly present me with some project for his future; but so far he is altogether silent. As you know I have condemned his invention as altogether worthless. Unfortunately Werner lacks all practical knowledge as a mechanical engineer and so I am powerless to obtain any engineering position for him. Concerning other work, here is the situation: all native Americans possess an excellent ingenuity that gives foreigners the greatest difficulty in earning a living to the extent that they lack practical experience in the field of technology. No country is more difficult than America for people who in Sweden are called 'gentlemen' to advance themselves. The want and wretchedness I see daily among this class of foreigners is unbelievable, and the difficulties I have with these unfortunates are so pressing that it disturbs my equanimity to some extent. I mention these conditions in order to temper your surprise that I have not already secured work for Werner. Hjalmar is entirely mistaken when in his letter he supposes that it would be easy for me to obtain a good job for your son.

"With deep sympathy and the warmest affection,
J. Ericsson"[10]

On the same day, Hjalmar's father wrote to him.

"I enclose an excerpt of a letter to Countess Ericson ... Just one angry addition: The man has no deep understanding of anything and so cannot get any position – As a salesman I think he could advance if he had any capital – and any prudence.

"Further testing shows that my new steam engine exceeds 15 horsepower..."[11]

In October, Ericsson writes Hjalmar, "It surprises me that in your last letter you have not mentioned my patent application for the Destroyer system, which I mailed to the Stockholm patent bureau almost four months ago. Italy gave me the patent a few days after receiving my application. That my native country would refuse what all other countries have given me with alacrity I can hardly imagine. ... I enclose a copy of the English patent, showing how liberally London's patent bureau treated me."[12]

Hjalmar's role as his father's representative now seems to have broadened to include functions of a patent agent. Hjalmar must have contacted the Patent Bureau, for Ericsson writes, in the next month:

"That my patent had been approved, I knew before *Norden* arrived. ...

"All I know about Werner Ericson's prospects you can learn from the enclosed exchange of letters between him and my secretary. The man is impossible to understand, and silent as the grave. According to what he told Taylor, his time this summer was devoted to certain mechanical inventions 'to earn some money.' ... That Werner has great faith in his new inventions you can conclude from the following expression during a conversation with Taylor, reported to me, i.e. 'Captain Werner Ericson stated emphatically, that he would not under any circumstances accept a *clerkship*.'

"As for the major project that brought Werner to America, I should mention that he still values craziness as highly as he did before he sought my advice. That under such circumstances it is not within my power to help Werner I think it unnecessary to say. All I can do, then, is to depend on the cash-box, for otherwise I fear that the crazy constructor will have to starve this winter – I hope I am mistaken."[13]

Writing Hjalmar again one week into the new year, Ericsson thanks him for his "especially well-done translation, it is excellent and I am very much in your debt for it."

Then he turns to another reason for gratitude:

"Werner Ericson departs within a few days for the Panama canal, to be hired as an engineer on this gigantic project. Since my brother Nils always praised Werner's skill as a canal builder, I could give him such a strong recommendation that the Panama canal's agent here immediately accepted him, but the specific job, the salary etc. the agent cannot decide. All he can do is pay for the passage [to Panama].

"Werner requires $200 dollars to buy suitable clothing for the hot climate and not to arrive there with empty pockets. This sum I have given him with the greatest pleasure, even though he had not conducted himself as I expected. Quite recently he answered an engineer who emphatically advised him to show me his invention 'I be dam'd if I do.' The details of his many 'inventions' all connected with the improvement of our times' undervalued steam engines I do not know, since Werner's confidants are not allowed to communicate them to me. One could say that this conceited and haughty man (which he is, in the highest degree) has been bitten by a mad steam engine builder. Through my secretary I know that his closest friends complain that he entirely lacks practical knowledge.

"During Werner's farewell visit yesterday, he let me know in an irritating way that he plans to return here to promote his inventions. My pain on hearing this I cannot describe since this shows that he is not going to devote all his powers to the position they are giving him at the Panama Canal."[14] But Ericsson was wrong. Werner remained in Panama for some years, and is said to have become the head of an administrative department of the canal project.[15]

In mid-April, 1882 Hjalmar wrote his father proudly that this winter his American snow plow had been put to use in the mountain regions with excellent results, and added that a rail line between the capital and Lilla Värtan [Stockholm's outer harbor], "a line that was built under my direct supervision," would be opened in May.[16]

Their correspondence continued at lengthening intervals, with requests from New York for newspapers, for translations, for intelligence of the Swedish defense posture (on which Ericsson still pinned his hopes of becoming the Swedish kingdom's Thor-like defender). But these requests were relatively rare and reasonable.

Ericsson's last letter of 1882 began:

"...I congratulate you heart and soul on the King's awarding you the Commander's Star of the Vasa Order..."[17] In 1867 Ericsson himself had received an award from the King of Sweden that Hjalmar's might be said to rival, but there is no hint of rivalry in his congratulations.

The presentation ceremonies had taken place on May 15. In a lofty chamber of the Royal Palace in Stockholm, Hjalmar advanced to receive the shining Vasa emblem from the hands of King Oscar II. Beside him Ludvig Nobel received the same.[18]

Brother of Alfred Nobel (who invented dynamite and bequeathed the Nobel Prizes) Ludvig was world-famous in his own right as the Oil King for his development of the prodigious Baku fields of Russia. It was into the circle of such celebrity, influence and power Hjalmar was being admitted.

Although there seems to be no record of who witnessed the ceremony, one can hope that the proud onlookers included Hjalmar's cousins John, now Baron Ericson, and Carl, now a major, and Nils' widow, Countess Wilhelmina von Schwerin Ericson; and Hjalmar's childhood companion, Professor Clas Theodor Odhner, whose brilliant historical writings would bring him into the Swedish Academy. Surely Sophie Fahlman Elworth was there. As the Swedish monarch placed the Vasa Order on its shining ribbon over her husband's shoulders Sophie might well have felt the soft descent of her own reward – for her faith and courage in marrying a made-up name and a secret.

Later, Hjalmar would receive from his father a request couched in these, for John Ericsson, remarkable terms: "I urge you to tell the King of the matters I have just related to you, if you believe it is your duty to do so."[19]

For Hjalmar Elworth, it had been a year of mounting recognition, appreciation, and public as well as private trust. To top it all, "Our main lines have operated at a profit during the last year," he wrote to John Ericsson, "to the great pleasure of us who direct them."[20] The Swedish national railway system was finally in the black. And so, one might say, was Hjalmar Elworth.

NOTES

1. Ericsson, John to Hjalmar Elworth, Dec. 2, 1880. The postscript is written in English.
2. Ericsson to Elworth, Dec. 17, 1880.
3. The allowance was generous for the time, but Ericsson emphasized that this support was gratuitous and limited by having Samuel W. Taylor write a note, short and entirely in English, to Werner (with a copy to Hjalmar): "When Baron Ericson lay on his death bed he sent for Professor Odhner [his sister Anna Carolina's son, Nils' nephew] whom he told that he had made no provision for the Odhner family, and that his Sisters [*sic*] must therefore look to their Uncle John.

"This, Professor Odhner informed Captain Ericsson by letter – Captain E. Immediately [*sic*] made his testament in favor of the Odhner family, altogether omitting to mention the Ericson family."

4. Ericsson to Elworth, Dec. 24, 1880.
5. Goldkuhl, Carola, 1967, 68-71. See also Hultqvist, 1993, 165, 168.
6. Elworth to Ericsson, Jan. 5, 1881.
7. Elworth to Ericsson, Feb. 20, 1881.
8. Ericsson to Elworth, Mar. 18, 1881.
9. Elworth to Ericsson, Apr. 11, 1881.
10. Ericsson to Wilhelmina Ericson, May 6, 1881.
11. Ericsson to Elworth, May 6, 1881.
12. Ericsson to Elworth, Oct. 7, 1881.
13. Ericsson to Elworth, Nov. 25, 1881.
14. Ericsson to Elworth, Jan. 6, 1882.
15. Werner only returned to Sweden in 1899, and died early in 1900. Wermelin, P.G., 1950, 25.
16. Elworth to Ericsson, Apr. 14, 1882 (Draft).
17. Ericsson to Elworth, Nov. 3, 1882.
18. *Sveriges Statskalender* 1883 , 455.
19. Ericsson to Elworth, Sept. 25, 1885.
20. Elworth to Ericsson, December 1882, in Goldkuhl, C., 1957, 125.

VI

Adieux

CHAPTER 22

A note from Hjalmar reached his father in April, 1883: "I send you the enclosed obituary in case you may have overlooked it."

Dated March 24, 1883, it told of "Carolina Christina née Lilliesköld, beloved wife of Professor C.J. Schlyter, dead at the age of 76 in Lund." On the clipping, Hjalmar's only comment was "Sophie is well and sends you cordial greetings. With filial regards, H. Elworth." Nothing more.

"How much you look like your mother!"

Perhaps the old man would see Carolina's face before him once again, feel again a complex loss. Or did this news simply set full stop to his sentence of exile?

Hjalmar had sent it to him, but without comment. His mother's identity had always been Elworth's deepest secret, even more shielded from his associates than the name of his father. If John Ericsson had inquired, when they met in New York in 1876, whether Hjalmar ever heard from his mother, the answer was almost certainly "Never." Professor Schlyter was said to lock his wife and children up in the house every day, when he went to teach his classes at Lund University! Thus one may easily doubt the other story, that Hjalmar received in Stockholm, every birthday, a bunch of violets from an unnamed sender.[1]

Finding the obituary, Hjalmar would have felt a sudden shock, but it was not grief. At age 59, he had certainly experienced grief. He had lost Brita Sofia, the grandmother who had taken him into her motherly care. He had lost his uncle Nils, his mentor and model. His aunt Anna Carolina Odhner, dead the same year, with whose family he had spent much of his boyhood. Friends who had died young, children of his cousins suddenly, unreasonably taken. In every case the loss stirred a multitude of associations, shared experiences, emotions in him, pain mingled with the dear remembrance.

But now he felt a sudden shock. A hollow impact. There was nothing to remember. Carolina Christina Lilliesköld had given him life. But almost at once she had given him away.

He had no portrait of her to drape in black. Indeed, he could not be sure what she looked like in life.

How meager his sense of her motherhood! The pang he felt might have been only at losing his last chance ever to meet her and discover her nature and thus to recapture a lost part of himself.

He clipped out the little item and dropped it in an envelope to John Ericsson.

NOTES

1. Goldkuhl, 1961, 58. But note Runvik, 1996, 151, citing date of obituary and brief contents of forwarding letter.

CHAPTER 23

John Ericsson was about to experience his last and most painful reversal of fortune.

When in 1876 he heard from Sweden that his son was about to travel to the United States and would visit him in New York, his first reaction was to rebuff closer acquaintance. He had worked out, over half a century's exile, loving Sweden at a certain distance, and he had been content to keep Hjalmar at the same scale.

Yet when they actually met face-to-face Hjalmar impressed him, and spurred a new train of thought. Ericsson's superb *Contributions to the Centennial Exhibition* volume was about to be published in New York. This demonstration of his thirty years of invention he hoped would renew his lease on being an American hero, but he wanted it to appear in Swedish as well. He had tried having various small samples of his text translated in New York, but these attempts did not yield results that satisfied him, perhaps because he did not wholly trust his own unassisted judgment of technical Swedish.[1] Perhaps Elworth, when he returned to Sweden, could be his "supervisor"? Maybe Hjalmar, from John Ericsson's detailed specifications and instructions, under his constant guidance, could launch a Swedish edition of *Contributions*? Ericsson considered himself a past master of such delegation.

He was able to persuade Hjalmar Elworth to undertake the task, though Elworth already had more than enough to do. However burdensome these new duties might become, they would keep him in touch with his father. He assented, and truly burdensome they became. But when the project was more than half done, Ericsson canceled his Swedish edition.

And yet Hjalmar had become his correspondent, his translator, his promoter, his agent, his emissary and, at last, his son. A son of whom he could well be proud. What could be more natural, then, than that John Ericsson would become his father? Ericsson himself was a devoted son. Yet how long it took him to undertake to be a father! And what a heavy price he must have paid for that postponement or abstention or demurral or denial of fatherhood, whatever it was!

After three score and ten years of lonely test and trial, no instant transformation could be expected, but John Ericsson began teaching himself to curb his hasty tongue, to entrust, to encourage and to express respect and appreciation.

He may even have begun to reconsider his own mortality, now that he felt he would be survived by a son.

But at the end of 1885 John Ericsson began to hear about Hjalmar's health.

"With deep pain," Ericsson wrote back, "I learn that you are suffering kidney problems. If you had never drunk the damnable Swedish punsch and sour wines your kidneys would be sound and healthy. Drink only ice water and weak tea and your pains will be assuaged, and because of the excellent body Nature has bestowed on you, you can hope to live without anguish once again."[2]

"My complaint," Hjalmar responded, "is now on the road to recovery, although it is going very slowly. Punsch is something I have seldom drunk and sour wines no oftener. I have probably brought this sickness on myself by my constant railroad travel, now on trains and now on handcars, in every kind of weather."[3]

("It was no pleasure trip to sit, day after day, on the open handcar and stop over and over again to investigate, to plan and to improve," according to the journal-keeper who accompanied Elworth on his many long inspection rounds. "But that is how Elworth knew his railroads all the way down to the ground....")[4]

"With anxiety," Ericsson wrote his son, "I am waiting for further word about your suffering." He added a p.s.: "I am still strong as a bear, with great working capacity – I work as many hours as ever, each day and night."[5]

"It makes us happy," Hjalmar responded, "to hear that you can still devote yourself with undiminished powers to your important experiments. As for me, I too have much to do and great working capacity, but my catarrh, that has now been found to be prostatic hypertrophy, gives me quite hard pain, especially because it prevents my getting any continuous sleep, forcing me to get up at least once an hour all night long. Our doctors here have no cure for this, only saying that one has to be satisfied not to get worse, for which purpose, every day, I irrigate my bladder with boric acid solution. ...

"We are staying for the summer in Södertälje, where, at those times I am free from inspection trips, I take warm sit-baths as prescribed by the doctor."[6]

Ericsson's reply told his son that "with a relieved anxiety I learn from your letter that your sickness derives from the enlargement of the prostate that is usual at your age."[7]

But this relief proved illusory, for the next letter Ericsson received from Hjalmar in Sweden, written at the beginning of November 1886, admitted that "during this time I have been quite sick, with a catarrh both of the stomach and of the bladder, having taken six weeks' leave to restore my health. First I used a mild water-cure and then, when it did no good, I took to my bed and used warm poultices on my bladder and perineum, which led to a noticeable relief from pain when passing urine. Last week I returned to work, and my condition seems to have gradually gotten better although I am compelled to empty my bladder 3 or 4 times a day.

"Most difficult of all is that I suffer from an extreme constipation that will not yield to the usual medications; however, I have now begun daily exercises that seem to be able to remove this evil. Since the first of August I have lost 17 pounds in weight, so that now I am quite thin and gaunt. ...

"Sophie's opinion is that I ought to travel to a more southerly climate to try to find a cure for my complaint, but since there is no certainty of success, I am reluctant to do so, as much because of the difficulties of travel as for the substantial expenses of it."[8]

This letter, newly opened, may have trembled in a hand that was trained for decades to avert tremor so as to draw a line of godlike steadiness. But now parallel lines, despite everything this 83-year-old man could do, converged.

Waiting in dread, the father did not answer his son's letter for six months.

He had little enough left. Now it was gone.

The stranger with his paper and pencil and little hammer -- Now he had finished what he came to Långbanshyttan to do –

Crack! Olof, my father
Crack! Brita, my mother
Crack! Anna Carolina, my sister
Crack! Nils, my brother
Crack! John Ericsson's rage boiled over –
Hjalmar
Hjalmar, my son!

Now it was gone.
He was what Captain Lillieskӧld, his lip curling, had called him:
"A man with no future!"

Ancient anger found new tinder and blazed up.

He destroyed all his copies of his correspondence before 1860. For good measure, he destroyed his entire shelf of diaries, his personal records of over five decades, to the startled dismay of William C. Church, who had undertaken to write his life's story.[9] No one was left to pass them to, these speculations and memories and mistakes and lessons.

He did not answer his son's letter for six months, and Hjalmar never wrote again. When Ericsson finally answered, on May 7, 1887, he wrote very strangely, in a tone of caustic reproof. It is hard not to conclude that he was thinking: If Hjalmar still lives, he is abandoning me. If he is dead, he has betrayed my trust.

"My dear Hjalmar,

... What you tell me concerning your sickness shows that ignorant doctors have destroyed your bladder. The difficulty in passing urine was not in the least the fault of the bladder. The usual enlargement of the prostate ... was the real reason for the difficulties, that is, for the hindrance in evacuation of the urine, especially with a full bladder. If you had immediately used a catheter and left your bladder alone instead of that damnable irrigation process, etc., you would now be well...

"I had much more to tell you on this subject, but you are unfortunately so conceited that advice is thrown away on you; you can even be rude to those who give you good advice. The content of my letter of August 6, it appears, was not important enough to mention, I did not even get a thank you for my good will. All this I deeply deplore, for the doctors' stupid treatments, approved by you in your wisdom, have made your prostate so sensitive, if not totally destroyed, that a cure seems distant if at all possible.

"Your complaint was originally of a completely mechanical nature, easy to overcome with simple mechanical means. Had you sought my advice in time you would now be as strong and healthy as before. ...

"May Providence strengthen you in your unhappy plight, and may your good common sense direct you in the future. These are the wishes of your
Warmly affectionate
J. Ericsson
P.S. Do you use a metallic or a flexible catheter?"[10]

But all this grief in the twisted form of reproach never received a reply from Hjalmar. Sophie Elworth answered Ericsson at once. She wrote an unflinching account of her husband's by now intense sufferings. Then she brought Hjalmar to Copenhagen in hopes of finding better medical treatment. The Danish doctors soon found there was nothing they could do and advised him to go home and prepare for death.

On the advice of friends, they broke their return journey in a small Swedish town called Jönköping, where there was a well-known sanitarium. Though at first the treatments seemed to bring some relief, quite suddenly on July12, 1887, Hjalmar Elworth died.[11]

Word of his death flashed by telegraph from station to station throughout the railroad network he had labored for years to extend into remotest Sweden.[12] His inspection trips had concerned the condition and safety of rails and structures, but many said that he also inquired about the needs of the people who worked with them. It was said that on these trips, over 20 years, he had visited two thousand homes of railroad workers.[13]

On the next Sunday a special train brought some 400 guests to a churchyard outside Jönköping, in a lovely spot lying between the railroad and Lake Vettern. Among these guests were railroad officials and rail workers, associates and friends, who entered the chapel between some 50 wreaths and floral decorations signed by organizations and individuals including his cousins Colonel Carl Ericson and Governor John Ericson. A 20-man choir sang hymns and there were simple prayers, though no formal eulogy.

Then eight men in railroad uniforms bore the casket out of the chapel, between solid ranks of railroaders from all parts of Sweden (3,000, according to one published report!), to the grave newly opened beside the railroad embankment. The choir sang again as Hjalmar's remains were put to rest.[14]

"This act made a peculiarly moving and gripping impression," a reporter observed. "On the high embankment the train was seen waiting, and the whole slope below it was filled with a tightly packed mass of people, while nearer the grave a compact wall was formed by a hundred railroad men in dress uniform, who had come to witness the last journey of their greatly loved and respected leader."[15]

NOTES

1. Ericsson, John to Axel Adlersparre, Dec. 24, 1864, includes the revealing statement: "Next time [I write to you] and from here on I plan to use English, to save time spent on editing and rewriting. Even though I have plenty of vocabulary in general subjects, it takes too much time to avoid obvious mistakes, and my technical language is so meager that I cannot at all say what I want in mechanical matters." Nevertheless, the overwhelming bulk of his many ensuing letters to Adlersparre on a great variety of subjects, technical and otherwise, are written in Swedish. This makes his switch to the English language years later, when calling Adlersparre to account for his unauthorized review of *Contributions* (see page 101) all the sharper.
2. Ericsson to Hjalmar Elworth, Jan. 8, 1886.
3. Elworth to Ericsson, Jan. 18, 1886.
4. Goldkuhl, Carola, 1957, 122.
5. Ericsson to Elworth, May 21, 1886.
6. Elworth to Ericsson, June 12, 1886.
7. Ericsson to Elworth, Aug. 6, 1886.
8. Elworth to Ericsson, Nov. 2, 1886.
9. Church, William C., 1906, ii, 307.
10. Ericsson to Elworth, May 7, 1887.
11. The death certificate, preserved among Elworth's papers at the Swedish

Railway Museum in Gavle, lists the cause of his death at an age of 63 years as "Primarily Cancer vesica urinaciae and secondarily uremia."

12. *Jernbanebladet*, Stockholm, Nr. 6, 1887, 42.
13. *Ny Illustrerad Tidning*, Stockholm, Aug. 13, 1887, 1 (Portrait); see also *Jernbanebladet*, Stockholm, Nr. 6, 1887, 42-3.
14. Jönköpings-Posten , Jönköping, July 14, 1887, and July 19, 1887.
15. Kungliga Biblioteket, Stockholm. Personal communication of Librarian Eva Dillman from KB's Obituaries Scrapbook, TU 31, of clippings dated but without attribution or page reference.

CHAPTER 24

The news of Hjalmar's death reached John Ericsson by telegram from Hjalmar's cousin John. A month later Sophie Elworth heard from her father-in-law:

"My dear Sophie,

The account in your letter of May 25 of Hjalmar's terrible condition was more painful than I can say. For that reason I later received the telegram from Baron Ericson with more satisfaction than sorrow, since death alone could relieve your husband's agonies. His body was apparently entirely destroyed by the ignorance of the doctors and his own folly. ...

"Kindly convey to your sister my thanks for her clear account of the funeral. Pompous funerals, in my opinion, are reprehensible, but in this case it was the friendship of his comrades that arranged all this unnecessary display. ... When your hand has recovered from its soreness I look for a few lines from you concerning the quiet and withdrawn life that now, with your small means, you prefer.

Your devoted friend, John Ericsson."[1]

Sophie Elworth would survive Hjalmar by 33 years. She remained in Jönköping where soon, in the churchyard beside the railroad embankment, a monument was raised by a subscription from every railroad worker in the national system. Into its black marble was incised the cryptic name "Hjalmar Elworth."

For a year and a half after Hjalmar's death, John Ericsson continued to spend his remarkable energies on a series of engines driven by the sun. He expressed great confidence that the exhaustion of conventional fuels was predictable and would some day require mankind to put the sun's enormous gift to useful work – and today, who can dispute that? These designs became, in "Harry" Delamater's great workshop, full-scale working models that the inventor subjected to elaborate testing on the roof of his house.

But in 1889, on the anniversary of *Monitor's* battle with the *Merrimack*, the inventor died in his sleep.

When Sophie heard of John Ericsson's death, she wrote to Samuel W. Taylor to ask whether there was any bequest, and to learn whether the famous man had ever acknowledged his son. Taylor responded with his own personal account of Ericsson's final days. For once it was Taylor's own English that impelled the elegant barque of his chancery hand:

"New York, March 29, 1889

Mrs. Sophie Elworth,

Stockholm

Madam!

"... Captain Ericsson, in assigning to me the duty of escorting Mr. Elworth for certain occasions, said: 'It is important for your guidance to know that I am his father.' I have not endeavored to learn more than this...

"Just before last Christmas Captain Ericsson conceived a new motive engine the working drawings for which, as customary, he made with his own hand, within 7 days, and he proudly alluded to the achievement as proof of his physical vigor and undiminished constructive energy; those around him, however, noticed his fatigue and feared that he had overtaxed himself.

"This engine, excepting the valve gear, was built and delivered at the Captain's residence by the 1st February; but a few days later all work was suspended, owing to the death of his very intimate friend, and looked-upon younger brother, C.H. Delamater, which bereavement there is no doubt was a terrible shock to him, however much he might, as he did, deny it. Fourteen days previously Captain Ericsson became somewhat lame and told me that he had sprained his ancle [*sic*] during gymnastic exercise – that he was mistaken is evident for, in a few days, a similar swelling was found in the other ancle and foot. He refused to seek medical advice, directing me to inform myself of the symptoms of 'dropsy.' To imagine that anything could be the matter with his kidneys was exceedingly disagreeable, so, not regarding my report and the facility with which he could himself have ascertained positive or negative indications, finding his pulse irregular, he jumped to the conclusion that his heart was not doing complete duty, remarking that 'a diagram of my pulse would resemble a saw with every sixth and 10th tooth broken off.'

"It was commanded that no mention of his ailment should be made to anyone; and the only course he adopted was dietary. Gradually he became quite lame, yet able to move around and do considerable work at his drawing table; and assuming such excellent spirits and happy disposition I readily agreed in his opinion that he would soon be in good order.

"On the 20th February, I again felt anxious and begged him to call in a physician but he became so angry that to persist would have been deemed impertinent; the Saturday following, however, he listened somewhat and consented to my being in his bedroom throughout the night, to discover the cause of his 'dreaming' which had disturbed and completely exhausted him each of the three previous nights. (Thus commenced my vigil of 300 hours with very few and short opportunities for rest.) He permitted me to witness his usual exercise before getting into bed, and its violent character astonished me as much as the manifest emaciation of his body pained me - my astonishment was so undisguised that subsequently he made a laughing allusion to it and listened to my supposition - that so much bodily labor was not conducive to maintaining an average weight especially on a diet, according to my notions, wanting in blood producing qualities - without resisting it, excepting that the food he took was the best for his digestive organs.

"His condition alternated, weaker and stronger; meanwhile I took the opportunity of stating a similar case to a medical friend and, fortified with sound matter-of-fact-reasons for the necessity of advice, I boldly and persistently pleaded with him. After short reflection he consented to an analytical test for albumen. He was, as I knew he would be, dissatisfied with the experts' report; and, with the object of showing me the inaccuracy of the analyst's diagnosis ordered me to have his water examined by a neighboring physician whom he had frequently called in for professional information. Doctor Boullee at once ascertained its low specific gravity and insisted on making a visit to explain personally the complications that were imminent.

"This was on Friday March 1st, from which time up to Tuesday evening he appeared to improve and at intervals gave me important instructions with his usual conciseness and vigor; near midnight a change took place and he was placed in bed Wednesday at 3 a.m. never afterwards to be dressed, although leaving bed when necessity required, sometimes unaided but carefully guarded. An old friend and eminent physician, Dr. Markoe was called in Wednesday noon.

"The Captain's greeting was remarkable as showing the direction of his thoughts. Raising himself, in a loud firm voice he asked 'Markoe, can a man who has Bright's disease of the kidneys do any more work?' And the measured, distinct reply 'Captain, a man who has Bright's disease of the kidneys has no right to do any more work' I felt to be the final dissipation of any hope the Captain entertained of again being useful to his fellow man and that now he would not make an effort to live.

"Captain Ericsson has many times alluded to '*death*' and his abhorrence of a long or painful illness - The doctors say that no suffering existed and he himself declared that he was 'resting very comfortably'; and I believe he died, if with feeling, as in going to sleep - exactly as he always hoped. His last words to me spoken one hour before, were: 'I am resting – this rest is magnificent; more beautiful than words can tell!'....
Respectfully, your obedient Servant,
S.W. Taylor, private secretary."[2]

But Samuel Taylor told his son a slightly different and more interesting story of Ericsson's final moments, which Frank H. Taylor related half a century later:

"When John Ericsson felt death approaching, he called my father and said to him,

'Taylor, get my checkbook and draw a check for $7,500.' Ericsson then signed the check with a hardly legible scribble. ... 'Go down and cash this check,' Ericsson continued, 'and keep my house open for a year. Pay all employees their usual salaries and pay all bills and charges, just as if I were here.'

"My father carried the check to the bank just as fast as he could walk. But rumors preceded him there to the effect that Ericsson was dead or dying. When the check was presented, the teller remarked, 'I hear that Ericsson is dead – is that so?' My father could only affirm that he had been alive when he left the house. 'Well,' said the teller, 'I have seen you come and go here and cash checks for the past thirty years or more, so I presume it is all right,' and handed him the cash. On my father's return with it, John Ericsson was dead – he had passed away half an hour before. My father used the money as instructed, and the house was kept running for a year."[3]

To Louis, Ericsson's manservant, and Ann Cassidy, his housekeeper, and Waldemar Lassöe, his drafting assistant, and to Samuel W. Taylor this transaction was a generous benefaction. But it may have served another purpose as well. It brought John Ericsson as much of the future as he could manage.

NOTES

1. Ericsson, John to Sophie Elworth, August 1887, in Goldkuhl, Carola, 1961, 237-8.
2. Taylor, Samuel W. to Sophie Elworth, Mar. 29, 1889. Curiously, Taylor opens his letter by acknowledging receipt of "your letter of March 9, 1876." Conceivably, Sophie was not confident that Taylor would recognize her name, and so as credentials for her inquiry enclosed a copy of an old letter to Ericsson. Quite possibly she had written the last of her secret appeals to Ericsson on that date, as soon as she knew Hjalmar was going to America. No Elworth letter to Ericsson of that date seems to have survived. It was in April of the same year that Baron John Ericson sent his uncle word of Hjalmar's impending American visit, which drew such a surprising rebuff from John Ericsson.
3. Taylor, Frank H., 1940, 7.

Epilogue

John Ericsson died in New York City on March 8, 1889, at age 85.

It had been 63 years since he left Sweden. A group of fellow officers in the Swedish Army, admiring his promise as an inventor and considering that England, where the Industrial Revolution was under way, would give his talents more scope, pooled the money for his trip.

Soon after he left in 1826, he wrote to his backers from London that he would return to Sweden "in a year, or never," preferring "the other side of the globe to returning home without fame."[1]

Probably meant to express his determination to succeed, this may instead have seemed a bit of bravado. But, in fact, when 13 years in England had brought him little more than lawsuits, confinements in debtors' prisons, and a troubled marriage, in 1839 he took ship for America with nothing but a promise of a project as his capital.

Though the project proved to be only the first of a series of painful reverses, his patent of the first effective marine propeller finally brought him a steady living. He was granted U.S. citizenship in 1848.

Another 13 years of hard work and the outbreak of the Civil War at last brought him his fame. Once his *Monitor* warship had preserved the Union's blockade of Confederate ports by turning back the *Merrimack*, the 37th Congress of the United States and the Legislature of New York State praised his "enterprise, skill, energy and forecast"; the New York Chamber of Commerce thanked him for saving the people of the United States from "a national disgrace, and disasters for which otherwise there could have been no remedy." A member of this Chamber added that "when the final hour of trial came ... the *Monitor*, almost unknown, with its magic presence appeared to give victory to our arms and forever make secure our harbors from a foreign attack."[2]

Others wove him and his 'ironclad' into the legends of the Civil War, with "The *Monitor* Grand March," "The *Monitor* Polka," "The Ericsson Galop," and

"Oh! Give us a Navy of Iron,
And to man it our Yankee Lads;
And we'll conquer the World's broad ocean
With our Navy of Ironclads."[3]

John Ericsson was even called by a Union general "the greatest man living."[4]

Yet he was not content.

In a letter to William Seward, American secretary of state, he said "I love Sweden and would willingly sacrifice my life for her honor."[5]

"I am certainly an American citizen," he had already written to the foreign minister of Sweden, "but nevertheless I consider it my greatest honor to be a Swedish subject. ... Should events require it, my life and all I own are at the service of his Majesty the King and my homeland."[6]

Later, his offer took on a darker tone. He wrote to his son Hjalmar in Sweden that "the homeland and everything that happens there... interests me ten times more than anything that happens in America. A short while ago I received from the secretary of the [Swedish] Academy of Military Sciences best wishes for 'my adopted homeland.' To this I answered, curtly, 'I recognize only one homeland. I would rather that my remains rest under a heap of stones on Swedish soil than under a marble monument in this country.'"[7]

Somebody was listening.

"On the day of [John Ericsson's] funeral," an eyewitness related, "the pall-bearers, thirty in number, his personal friends, and the representatives of various societies, Swedish and others, gathered at the desolate house in Beach Street. From there they proceeded in carriages, and without ceremony, to Trinity Church, in lower Broadway. It was filled with Delamater's 700 workmen, with members of the Scandinavian community and, closest to the coffin, Ann Cassidy, Taylor, Lassöe and the Swedish...consul. The rector of Trinity Church had been the chaplain on board the *U.S.S. Minnesota* in 1862 [when, in Hampton Roads, the *Monitor* intervened to prevent the Confederate ironclad from destroying it where it lay aground]. He read the Burial Service, and the fine choir sang Cardinal Newman's noble hymn - "Lead, kindly light." On the coffin, with other tributes, lay two beautiful palm leaves tied with a broad black ribbon and bearing this inscription, *Fältjägares [Riflemen's] Regiment, Royal Swedish Army.* No offering could have been more grateful, for with [this regiment] Ericsson's dearest recollections were associated. ...

"On the east side of New York City is located the 'Marble Cemetery,' dating back to the time of James Monroe, fifth President of the United States, who was buried there in 1831.... To this cemetery his body was carried and placed in a receiving vault to await a decision as to its final resting place. ..." The account, by William C. Church, Ericsson's authorized biographer, continues:

"A month after Ericsson's burial, this communication was sent to the secretary of state from the legation of the United States at Stockholm: ... *Sweden would regard with extreme favor Ericsson's body sent home by man-of-war."* ...

"In June, 1890 ...the *Baltimore*, a fine cruiser under the command of Captain W.S. Schley, U.S.N. ... was the vessel finally chosen." ...

"On August 18, 1890, the Acting Secretary of the Navy issued an order reading, in part:

"...It is the desire of the President to give solemn expression to the cordial and fraternal feeling that unites us with a kindred people, the parent source of a large body of our most valuable citizens, of whom the late inventor...was the most illustrious example.

"In recognition of this feeling and of the debt we owe to Sweden for the gift of Ericsson, whose genius rendered us the highest service in a moment of grave peril and anxiety, it is directed that... when we give back his body to his native country, the flag of Sweden shall be saluted by the squadron. ...

"As the *Baltimore* gets under way and passes the vessels of the squadron, each vessel will masthead her colors, display the Swedish ensign, and fire a national salute of twenty-one guns. The *Baltimore* will immediately proceed to sea.

"By command of the President....[8]

Gothenburg, Sweden's greatest port, was the *Baltimore*'s announced destination. But soon Stockholm, as the capital, preempted the honor of receiving John Ericsson's remains. Nevertheless the governing board of the Gothenburg Workers' Confederation announced an Ericsson memorial ceremony to be held the same day the great inventor's remains were received in Stockholm. Not to be outdone, Malmö's Order of Good Templars declared that all their Malmö lodges would solemnize the same Stockholm arrival with tributes and ceremonies. The city of Kristinehamn, too, would honor Ericsson's return to his homeland with solemn rites.[9]

Stockholm's plans were of a higher caliber. The Jämtland Riflemen's regiment in which young John had served as a surveying officer announced that its commander would be among the official party receiving the remains of the illustrious inventor. So would Colonel Carl Ericson, son of John's late brother Nils. The Royal Swedish Society of Naval Sciences would send an admiral and other high officers. The Royal Swedish Academy of Military Sciences, the Royal Swedish Academy of Sciences and the Swedish Engineering Society would all be represented, along with a deputation of professors headed by the rector of Uppsala University.

All these plans were published in the leading newspapers while the *U.S.S. Baltimore* was still at sea. Already a controversy had arisen over just where John Ericsson's body would be buried. The king himself settled the argument in favor of scenic Filipstad, rather than the nearby mining village where Ericsson had been born, Långbanshyttan.

BALTIMORE AT GOTHENBURG proclaimed the newspaper headline of an extra edition published on September 9. As soon as the visitor's "beautiful white hull" had been sighted at 6:30 a.m., the Gothenburg harbor pilot steamed out to deliver dispatches to the cruiser's commanding officer. These were orders diverting it to Stockholm. By 8:00 a.m. the cruiser *Baltimore* had hoisted its anchor and continued its voyage, now toward the capital.[10]

But Malmö had not, after all, awaited either the landfall of the *Baltimore* or the landing of Ericsson's mortal remains to commemorate the hero's return. Already on Sunday, September 7 a memorial service was held in St. Petri church where over 3,000 persons prayed and sang amid green and blooming decorations surmounted by the initials of John Ericsson's name, each 4 feet high, in living gas flames which also formed a shining sun above and a laurel wreath below.[11]

The city of Eskiltuna, too, celebrated the inventor's memory early, with "a procession of sharpshooters and Temperance Union members."[12]

Work had already started at Stockholm's great Central Station on the conversion of a railway flatcar into a funerary conveyance. Ericsson's body would be borne in state to Filipstad over the railroad network Nils Ericson had brought into being and John's son Hjalmar Elworth had directed. The catafalque would rest on the flatcar under a wooden structure 14 feet high but open to each side, under a canopy of black velvet sprinkled with stars of silver.

But the moment when John Ericsson's body was returned to Swedish soil would first be celebrated within another structure. A grand pavilion 60 feet high was being erected on quayside in Stockholm harbor, near the statue of Sweden's famous warrior king Carl XII, opposite the Swedish royal castle. From the pavilion's five peaks both the Swedish and the American flags would wave.[13]

Early on the misty morning of the 13th of September, the headlines announced BALTIMORE IS HERE! "At last the white hull became visible... It grew and stretched out to gigantic proportions, that the mist further magnified... From a long row of portholes a soft electric light glowed as the colossus glided majestically forward over the glassy calm" of the Stockholm harbor, parting the lanterns of a crowd of smaller vessels. *U.S.S. Baltimore* cast anchor in Stockholm at 7:15 a.m. on Saturday, September 13.

Witnesses on the shore were "suddenly overwhelmed by the feeling that this vision was unique. Never had the remains of any mighty ruler, never that of any victory-crowned sea hero been paraded on such a stately catafalque."[14]

The *Baltimore*'s crew of 400 remained aboard pending the next day's great events. "An oaken coffin rested on the afterdeck, covered by sailcloth," it was reported. "Atop it is a golden plaque inscribed 'Captain John Ericsson, Died March 8, 1889. Aged 85 years.'"[15]

A great trove of wreaths had been sent along by admiring Swedish-Americans, including one from the "Freya Swedish ladies" of New York. Their wreath pictured Ericsson's *Monitor* in flowers, with flags of both nations and a dove of peace.[16]

Sunday dawned bright and clear. An excited throng estimated at well over 150,000 persons had come from many parts of Sweden to line the shores of the harbor and stand on the roofs of adjoining buildings. Some had even climbed into the branches of trees.

In the afternoon a royal steam launch brought to the ship those Swedes who had been chosen to receive John Ericsson's body. There were speeches by the American minister and a Swedish admiral, and by Ericsson's nephew Colonel Carl Ericson. Then, with military honors laced with trumpet acclamations, the coffin was lowered from the warship into the launch.

At precisely 2:00 in the afternoon the battery on the quay below the royal palace roared a salute. As *Baltimore*'s big guns thundered a reply, the royal palace flag was lowered to half mast – a singular honor. The launch, draped in black but decorated with silver crowns and both nations' bright flags, set out for shore, to accomplish John Ericsson's return, so long delayed, to Swedish soil.

While a funeral march was played the coffin was borne from the landing place to the lofty pavilion, crowned in all four directions with laurel that had been prepared. Many more wreaths were brought and presented while a military chorus of 200 sang, and memorial verses were read.[17] The seated audience included Ericsson family members, including "the widow of Ericsson's acknowledged son, Director Elworth."[18]

At the conclusion of these ceremonies the bells of all the Stockholm churches began to toll as the cortege set out for the Central Station, from which John Ericsson's remains would be conveyed to their last resting place in Filipstad.

A mounted detachment of Royal Guards led the procession, followed by the hearse with pallbearers marching along on each side. Next came carriages conveying the representatives of Sweden's king and crown prince, the American ambassador and the captain of the *Baltimore*, city officials and the Ericsson family. Behind these carriages a long procession advanced on foot, led by officers of the Royal Navy, of the *U.S.S. Baltimore* and of the Swedish Army's Riflemen's Regiment, Ericsson's old outfit from the Jämtland northern frontier.

Walking behind them came delegations and deputations of a motley variety of Swedish organizations. Yet still other representatives defined the parade route itself. As many as a hundred different associations had undertaken to station their members, men and women displaying colorful banners and sashes and ribbons, along the way to add both distinction and crowd control to the tribute. Thus the royal academies of sciences and of military sciences and the faculties of Uppsala, Lund and other universities took official part, but also the Stockholm Workers' Association, the Gothenburg Association of Machinists, the Odd Fellows Lodge, and the temperance societies.[19] Over 5,000 persons took part in the procession in one way or another.[20]

Swedes had heard a lot about John Ericsson's international fame. His gifts to Sweden for the nation's defense and his generous benefactions when Swedish crops failed all had kept his name bright among his countrymen. But there may have been something more driving this remarkable, this truly prodigal fervor.

The tide of Swedes emigrating to America had recently crested at over 46,000 in a single year, a phenomenon called "America fever." Swedish officials must have felt a mounting concern over this drain of the most enterprising among their relatively small population. The return of Ericsson, their most successful emigrant, even posthumously, may have seemed an opportunity to dramatize nationality and loyalty. They would not have been slow to approve and to finance elaborate celebrations and commemorations in the hope that these might cool the "fever."

The Swedish man in the street may have had another kind of motive. For all those who stayed behind when their sons, daughters and other kin ventured over the sea to a new world, celebrating the success in America of John Ericsson may have been a kind of talisman to assure the good luck of their absent pioneers.

As the cortege bearing the remains of the American citizen who chose to remain a subject of the Swedish king crossed the thronged plaza before the Central Railroad Station, another detachment of Royal Guards snapped to attention, the tolling of church bells ceased and a military band struck up a funeral march. The inventor's coffin was borne through the station between ranks of railroad officials, out onto the platform. It was placed upon the black-draped open-sided funerary car, part of a special 10-car train bound for Filipstad. A score of massive wreaths, one picturing Ericsson's *Monitor* in leaves and flowers, were laid upon the coffin. The royal and diplomatic officials, the Ericsson family members, reporters from the leading newspapers, and representatives from the town of Filipstad boarded the train. A final salute thundered from the cannons back at quayside in the harbor as the train quietly and slowly glided from the station in the late afternoon's waning light.[21]

The train gained speed passing through Riddarholmen and Stadsgården and Liljeholmen (where building a railroad tunnel through the high ridge had brought distinction to the young Hjalmar Elworth, John's son, while John's brother Nils Ericson was still the dynamic head of Sweden's new railway network). There was no pause at a whistle stop called Gnesta but it surprised everyone by its handsome decorations including the initials "J.E." in flowers mounted below the station clock. But in the gathering dusk, as the train entered Stjernhof, suddenly "no less than 40 electric light bulbs spread their clear light over John Ericsson's funerary car in the quiet, still night." "This created a magnificent effect," according to more than one reporter.

A multitude of torches illuminated the arrival in Katrineholm, where a crowd of "more than a thousand" had assembled to greet the train. The Good Templars lodge, the Workers' Association and the Society of a Hundred, "all of them with their banners," paid tribute. Torches, too, greeted the train in Laxå, and in Hallsberg "huge crowds" were waiting, and "right in the middle of the platform was seen a transparency of a moving propeller..." "The reception in Hallsberg was one of the most solemnly impressive," a correspondent for a Stockholm paper wrote, "and the number of persons approached two thousand."[22]

By the morning of September 15 the train had reached its destination, Filipstad. On the platform waited a committee headed by the governor and the bishop, and a throng that overflowed the tracks. Twelve miners from Ericsson's village, Långbanshyttan, bore his coffin through a triumphal arch to place it on a rose-covered catafalque.[23]

In the festively decorated church, Bishop Rundgren celebrated the funeral rites.

"The temple has been opened for our illustrious native son," he declared. "Joyous multitudes have assembled around his bier. Every heart exults over owning him once more, though saddened that life must be harvested by death.

"Yet he who has labored nobly lives on in our memories. Long, long will it be until John Ericsson's name is forgotten either here or anywhere in his homeland.

"What we offer you," the bishop said to the returning hero, "is three spadesful of Sweden's earth on Lake Daglösen's lovely shore. Rest here in peace after a life of challenge and struggle! Not only were you a great man, but also a noble one. Your heart was touched by all human suffering. In carrying out your great works, you thought not of yourself, but of your homeland. You were a Swede and you remained Swedish in your heart and soul. We thank you for that, we thank you for everything!

"And now, farewell, farewell!"[24]

A paradoxical greeting to John Ericsson.

The ultimate exile.

———

NOTES

1. Ericsson to A.F. Gussander, Nov. 26, 1826, in Lindwall, 1937, 68-70.
2. Church, William C., 1906, i, 294-5, 297.
3. "The Monitor Grand March," by Edward Mack. (Philadelphia: Lee & Walker, c. 1862) Sheet music in the New York Public Library Digital Gallery. "Monitor Polka," by G. Weingarten. (New York: H.B. Dodsworth, 1862). Sheet music dedicated "To Captain Ericsson" in the Civil War Sheet Music Collection, Library of Congress."The Ericsson Galop," by V. Tinans. (Boston: Oliver Ditson & Co., c. 1862). Sheet music dedicated "to the inventor of the celebrated Steam Battery MONITOR" in the 'I Hear America Singing' collection, Library of Congress. "Oh! Give us a Navy of Iron" with words by D. Brainerd Williamson, music by Jas. W. Porter. (Philadelphia: J.W. Lawton & Co., c. 1862). Sheet music dedicated "to Capt. John Ericsson, Inventor of the Monitor" in Historic American Sheet Music collection, Digital Scriptorium, Rare Book, Manuscript and Special Collections Library, Duke University.
4. Stimers, Alban C. To John Ericsson, 1862, in Church, William C., *op.cit*, i, 290.
5. Church, William C., *op. cit*, ii, 122.
6. Ericsson to Count Carl Wachtmeister August 13, 1864, in Runvik, Margaretha, 1996, p. 130.
7. Ericsson to Hjalmar Elworth, Nov. 2, 1877.
8. Church, William C., *ibid.*, 323-329.
9. My account of Ericsson commemorative events in Sweden is based on contemporary news coverage, including eyewitness reports, published in 1890, in the following Swedish newspapers:
   Dagens Nyheter [Daily News], Stockholm - aka "DN"
   Skånska Aftonbladet [Skanian Evening News], Malmö - aka "SkA"
   Svenska Dagbladet [Swedish Daily News], Stockholm - aka "SvD"
   Advanced planning by officials in Gothenburg, Malmö, Kristinehamn and Stockholm while the *U.S.S. Baltimore* was still at sea are described in SvD, September 5, 1890.
10. The warship's arrival in Gothenburg is described in DN, Sept. 9, 1890.
11. Malmö's memorial service held before the arrival in Sweden of Ericsson's remains was described in SkA, September 6 and 8, 1890.
12. The procession in Eskiltuna was described in DN, September 8, 1890. In his later years, Ericsson had been a prominent supporter of temperance causes.
13. The structure that would house Ericsson's coffin during ceremonies celebrating his return to Swedish soil was described in SvD on September 5, 1890.
14. The impressions of those who sighted Baltimore's huge hull in the mist, portholes aglow with electric light, are described in DN's issue of September 13, 1890. Electric light was evidently a mysterious novelty in Sweden at the time.
15. This description of the coffin and its identifying plaque was actually pub-

lished in DN on September 9, 1890, after its intrepid reporter talked his way onto the cruiser in Gothenburg while it was preparing, with new orders, to leave for Stockholm.

16. Swedish reporters describe not only wreaths brought to Sweden from New York but also other wreaths presented at every stop, from Stockholm to Filipstad. Apparently many wreaths featured decorations representing the *Monitor*, devised as a lethal instrument of war, in flowers with doves of peace. Perhaps the already venerable Swedish tradition of armed neutrality was exerting an influence!
17. DN, Sept. 15, 1890, and SvD, same date.
18. Sophie Elworth's role in the family as the widow of "Ericsson's acknowledged son" was mentioned in SkA, Sept. 15, 1890. This must have been doubly gratifying for Sophie, who had early written in vain to the great man secretly pleading for Hjalmar's acknowledgment, and later, when Ericsson had met his son in America, would have known what efforts the 11-year-long relationship had cost Hjalmar.
19. SvD, Sept. 15, 1890.
20. DN, Sept. 15, 1890.
21. SvD, Sept. 15, 1890 and SkA, same date.
22. DN, Sept. 15, 1890.
23. DN, Sept. 16, 1890.
24. Grip, Elias, 1920. 149-150.

Works Cited in the Text

Correspondence
Excerpts from some 80 letters between John Ericsson and Hjalmar Elworth are quoted in this book. All were written in Swedish. I have been a translator from Swedish to English for over 40 years. Every Swedish letter from which I have quoted is my own translation, with this exception: Ericsson's authorized biographer, William C. Church, quoted from translations he had obtained, but sometimes omitted to give either the name of Ericsson's correspondent or the exact date of the letter. Where my endnote identifying a quoted letter refers only to Church's biography, it may be assumed that the translation quoted is not my own, since the Swedish original may not have been available to me.

Books and Articles
Adelsköld, C. L. *John Ericsson: Biografiska teckningar* [John Ericsson: Biographical Notes]. Stockholm, 1894.
Adelswärd, Baron to his mother, May 26, 1856. Private communication from Johan T. Adelswärd, Nov. 22, 2002, furnishing a facsimile of his 'excerpt copy in Swedish...the original letters are in French.'
Bayard, Samuel J. A Sketch of the Life of Commodore Robert F. Stockton. New York, 1856.
Bonsdorff, Leo. "*Göteborgshamn* [Gothenburg Harbor]" in *Vår Flotta* [Our Navy], November, 1907. *Göteborgs hamn genom tiderna* [Gothenburg Harbor Through History].Gothenburg, 1931.
Brugge, Bengt. *"John Ericsson 1803-1889,"* in *Öviks-och-Myssjöbygden, No. 33,* 1989, 33-93.
Church, William C. *Life of John Ericsson*. New York, vol. 1, 1906; vol. 2, 1907.
Dardel, Fritz von. *Dagboksanteckningar* [Diaries] vol. 5, 1873-1876. Stockholm, 1916.
Dorr, Ebenezer P. "The first Monitor and its inventor." A paper read before Buffalo Historical Society. Buffalo, N.Y., 1874. [Note pp. 50-51 the important eyewitness statement of Captain James Byers concerning the badly damaged condition of the *Merrimack* when it left Hampton Roads after its battle with the *Monitor.*]
Ekström, Gustaf. *Baltzar von Platen och Göta Kanal* [Baltzar von Platen and the Göta Canal]. Stockholm, 1938.
Elworth, Hjalmar. *Rese-Berättelse* [Travel Report] as follows:
1876a. Handwritten draft in brown leatherbound notebook 4 x 6 1/2 inches, 150 pages, with trademark 'R. Magee & Son, Stationers, 808

Chestnut St., Philadelphia.' Collection of the Swedish Railway Museum, Gävle.
1876b. Excerpts of 1876a, above, under title "*Om amerikanska jernvägars konstruktion och traffikerande m.m.* [Concerning the construction and operation of American railroads, etc.]" in *Jernbanebladet* [Railroad News], Nos. 11 (pp. 3-5) & 12 (pp. 3-8), Nov. & Dec. 1876.
1876c. Excerpt of 1876b, above, under title ' *Amerikanska snöplogar* [American Snow Plows]' in *Ingeniörs-Föreningens Förhandlingar för 1876* [Proceedings of the Engineering Society for 1876] p. 143 and Plates 24 & 25.
1877. Section X, *Jernvägsmaterial, m.m.* [Railway Equipment, etc.] in *Redogörelser för Verldsutställningen i Filadelfia 1876 utgifna till Kongl. Utställningskommitté* [Report on the World's Exhibition in Philadelphia, 1876 for the Royal Exhibitions Committee]. Stockholm, 1877. Section X, pp. 354-383 and (separately bound illustrations) Plates XXXIII - XLI.
Ericsson, John.
1876a. *Contributions to the Centennial Exhibition.* Brochure of 56 pages, printed by John Ross & Company, New York.
1876b. *Contributions to the Centennial Exhibition.* Book of 570 pages, "printed for the author at 'The Nation' Press, New York."
1879. "Excerpt from a letter regarding the Ericsson family," Stockholm, 1879.
Ericson, Nils. *Undertecknads Lefnadshändelser* [Events of My Life], autobiographical summary statement submitted 1845 on election to Royal Swedish Academy of Sciences, Stockholm.
Fröding, H. *Det forna Göteborg: Biografiska och kulturhistoriska studier* [Gothenburg in the Past: Studies in Biographical and Cultural History]. Originally written for *Göteborgs Handels och Sjöfarts-Tidning.* 1903.
Goldkuhl Carola. "*Hjalmar Elworth 1824-1887*" in *Daedalus, Tekniska Museets Årsbok 1957* [Daedalus, Yearbook of the National Museum of Science and Technology, Stockholm, for 1957] pp. 108-125.
Goldkuhl, Carola. "*John Ericssons brevväxling* [John Ericsson's Correspondence]" in *Daedalus 1958*, pp. 75-90.
Goldkuhl Carola. *John Ericsson: Mannen och uppfinnaren* [John Ericsson: The Man and the Inventor]. Stockholm,1961.
Goldkuhl, Carola. "Nils Ericsson - Mannen och ingenjören [Nils Ericsson - The Man and the Engineer]" in *Daedalus 1966* (pp. 75-110), *1967* (pp. 31-80).
Grip, Elias. *John Ericsson: En livsbild* [John Ericsson – a life portrait]. Uppsala, 1920.

Hagerman, Maja. *Berättelser från utlandet: Svenska tekniker...på utresor i...Amerika under 1800-talets senare hälft* [Narratives from Foreign Lands: Swedish technical travelers in America during the second half of the 1800s]. Stockholm, 1981.
Hallerdt, Björn. *Propellerns pionjär och Monitors mästare: Glimtar av John Ericssons liv och verk* [Pioneer of the Propeller and Master of the Monitor: Glimpses of John Ericsson's Life and Work]. Stockholm, 2003.
Hone, Philip. Diary 1828-1851. New York, 1970.
Hultman, Holter. *Långbanshyttan i forna tider* [Långbanshyttan in the Past]. Filipstad, 1949.
Hultqvist, Per. "Hundratals mil... Nils Ericson och moderniseringen av 1800tals Sverige"[Hundreds of leagues... Nils Ericson and the modernization of 19th century Sweden] in *Den svenska historien* [Swedish History], yearbook of *Älvsborgs Länsmuseum*, Vänersborg, Sweden, 1993.
Jansson, Ingrid. *"Svensk rapportering av amerikansk teknologi på världsutställning i Philadelphia 1876* [Swedish Reporting on American Technology at the Philadelphia World's Fair 1876]." In Stockholm Papers in History and Philosophy of Technology, Stockholm, 1980.
Lindqvist, Herman. *Historien om Sverige: Del VI, När riket sprängdes och Bernadotte blev kung* [The History of Sweden: Part VI, When the kingdom was shattered and Bernadotte became king]. Stockholm, 1998.
Lindwall, Gustaf. *Ingeniören vid Beach Street: John Ericssons liv i ny belysning* [The Engineer on Beach Street: New Light on John Ericsson's Life]. Stockholm, 1937.
MacCord, Charles W. "Ericsson and His Monitor," in *North American Review*, October, 1889, pp. 460-71.
Miles, Capt. A. H., USN. "The 'Princeton' Explosion" condensed from the U.S. Naval Institute Proceedings, v. 52, no. 285, November 1926, in *The Iron Worker*, Spring, 1957, pp. 1-11.
Mindell, David A. War, Technology and Experience aboard the *USS Monitor*. Baltimore, 2000.
Princeton University Seeley G. Mudd Manuscript Library, Historical Subject File. Undated document headed "Clerk's Office, Borough of Princeton, N.J., 'The U.S.S.Princeton,'" and page 2 addendum on "Special meeting of Council held on the morning of September 5, 1843..." Personal communication Feb. 6, 2002 from Tad Bennicoff, Special Collections Assistant, Seeley G. Mudd Manuscript Library.
Randel, William P. Centennial: American Life in 1876. Philadelphia, 1969.
Robinson, George H. "Recollections of John Ericsson" an address before the Commercial Club, Providence, R.I., Mar. 24, 1894.

Rubenson, Mauritz. *Skildringar från Amerika och England* [Sketches from America and England]. Stockholm, 1868.
Runvik, Margaretha Jönsson. *John Ericsson: Resan mot solen* [John Ericsson: Voyage Toward the Sun]. Karlstad, 1996.
Schildt, Göran. *Resenärer i Flores rike* [Travelers in the Kingdom of Flowers]. Stockholm, 1960.
Sioussat, St. George L. "The Accident on Board the U.S.S. 'Princeton,' February 28, 1844: A Contemporary Newsletter," in *Pennsylvania History*, July 1937. Reproduces account of witness Congressman George Sykes sent in a letter to his sister.
Skarstedt, Ernst S . *Svensk-amerikanska folket i helg och söcken* [The Swedish- Americans on Holidays and Everydays]. Stockholm, 1917.
Still, William N., Jr. Monitor Builders: A historical study of the principal firms and individuals... Washington, D.C. 1988.
Strömbäck, Lars. *Baltzar von Platen, Thomas Telford och Göta kanalen: Entreprenörskap och tekniköverföring i brytningstid* [Baltzar von Platen, Thomas Telford and the Göta Canal: Entrepreneurship and Technology Transfer in a Time of Transition]. Stockholm, 1993.
Sverigeboken [A Book About Sweden]. Stockholm, 1982.
Sveriges Statskalender 1883. XI, Kongl. Svenska Riddar-Ordnarne [Yearbook of the Swedish Government for the year 1883. Chapter XI, Royal Swedish Honors].
Taylor, Frank H. "Glimpses from John Ericsson's Private Life," in Bulletin of the American Society of Swedish Engineers, Mar. 1940, pp. 6-7.
Trout, S. Edgar. The Story of the Centennial of 1876: Golden Anniversary. Historical Society of Pennsylvania, Philadelphia, 1929.
Welles, Gideon. Diary of Gideon Welles: Secretary of the Navy Under Lincoln and Johnson [1861-1869]. Eds., H.K. Beale & A.W. Brownsword. New York, 1960.
Wells, William S. The Story of the Monitor. New Haven, 1899.
Wermelin, Per G. *Wargöns Aktiebolag 1874-1949* [Wargön Inc. 1874-1949]. Pp. 16-50 *"En stormans livsverk.* [The life's work of a great man]. " Gothenburg, 1950.
West, Richard S., Jr. Mr. Lincoln's Navy. New York, 1957.
Westerlund, Kerstin. *Christopher Polhem: Konstruktör och företagare i 1700-talets Sverige* [Christopher Polhem: Constructor and Entrepreneur in 18th-Century Sweden]. Stockholm, 2000.
White, Ruth M. Yankee from Sweden: The Dream and the Reality in the Days of John Ericsson. New York, 1960.
Whitman, Walt. "Battle of Bull Run, July 1861" in Specimen Days, and Collect, Glasgow, 1883.

Newspapers
New York Sunday Mercury, Oct. 22, 1843, p. 2, "Race on the Ocean."
Philadelphia Public Ledger, Oct. 3, 1843; Oct. 16, 1843; Oct. 20, 1843.
Swedish newspaper and magazine coverage of Elworth commemorative events, 1887:
Jernbanebladet [Railroad News], Stockholm
Jönköpings-Posten [Jönköping Post], Jönköping
Ny Illustrerad Tidning [New Illustrated Magazine]
Swedish newspaper coverage of Ericsson commemorative events,1890:
Dagens Nyheter [Daily News], Stockholm
Skånska Aftonbladet [Skanian Evening News], Malmö
Svenska Dagbladet [Swedish Daily News], Stockholm

Name Index

About the Author

David Mel Paul was awarded the M.A. in Humanities by the University of Chicago and received a Swedish language certificate from Uppsala University in Sweden.

He served for three years in the U.S. Navy, became a technical writer and then an exhibit designer and producer in aerospace companies. For the U.S. Department of Commerce he spent a year interviewing scientists, including several Nobelists, and scripting the exhibits about their most famous experiments that were featured in the U.S. Science Pavilion in the Seattle World's Fair, 1962.

He joined the United States Information Agency as a producer of cultural exchange exhibitions, organizing the U.S. pavilion in the First Asian International Trade Fair in Bangkok, Thailand, 1966. Over his ensuing 30-year USIA career he was sent to Leningrad and Kiev, to East Berlin, Bucharest, Budapest, Prague, Vienna and Warsaw, and to Athens, Buenos Aires and Beijing with exhibits he and his team developed about American life, lifestyle, science and history.

Margareta Paul, who first taught him Swedish, was stationed at the Swedish Embassy in Washington when they met. They have been married 52 years and have two sons and five grandchildren. He became a translator of Swedish books; a variety of American publishers have issued his English versions of Swedish biography and fiction.

Made in the USA
Middletown, DE
24 October 2016